FRACTURE MECHANICS OF COMPOSITES

A symposium
sponsored by ASTM
Committee D-30 on High Modulus
Fibers and Their Composites
AMERICAN SOCIETY FOR
TESTING AND MATERIALS
Gaithersburg, Md., 25 Sept. 1974

ASTM SPECIAL TECHNICAL PUBLICATION 593
G. P. Sendeckyj, symposium chairman

List price $23.50
04-593000-33

AMERICAN SOCIETY FOR TESTING AND MATERIALS
1916 Race Street, Philadelphia, Pa. 19103

Printed in Baltimore, Md.
November 1975

Foreword

The Symposium on Fracture Mechanics of Composites was held at the National Bureau of Standards, Gaithersburg, Md., on 25 Sept. 1975. ASTM Committee D-30 on High Modulus Fibers and Their Composites sponsored the symposium. G. P. Sendeckyj, Air Force Flight Dynamics Laboratory, presided as the symposium chairman.

Related
ASTM Publications

Composite Materials: Testing and Design, STP 546 (1974), $39.75, 04-546000-33

Applications of Composite Materials, STP 524 (1973), $16.75, 04-524000-33

Analysis of the Test Methods for High Modulus Fibers and Composites, STP 521 (1973), $30.75, 04-521000-33

A Note of Appreciation
to Reviewers

This publication is made possible by the authors and, also, the unheralded efforts of the reviewers. This body of technical experts whose dedication, sacrifice of time and effort, and collective wisdom in reviewing the papers must be acknowledged. The quality level of ASTM publications is a direct function of their respected opinions. On behalf of ASTM we acknowledge with appreciation their contribution.

ASTM Committee on Publications

Editorial Staff

Contents

Introduction

During the past decade, high-performance fiber reinforced composites have evolved from a laboratory curiosity to viable structural materials. Pacing this evolution has been a strong research effort involving the development of analysis and test methods coupled strongly with the introduction of fiber reinforced composites possessing consistently reproducible properties. With the mechanics of composites being reasonably well understood, research emphasis has shifted towards gaining an understanding of the fatigue and fracture response of composite materials.

This publication is the proceedings of a one-day meeting, organized by the American Society for Testing and Materials Committee D-30 on High Modulus Fibers and Their Composites, with the goal of bringing together analysts and experimentalists working in the fracture of composites area. As can be seen from the papers in the volume, the goal has been achieved.

The theoretical papers present a state-of-the-art review of analysis methods developed for studying the complex phenomena associated with the fracture processes in composite laminates. The first three papers address the very difficult problem of determining the three-dimensional stress distribution in the vicinity of through the thickness crack with and without crack tip damage. The next two papers address the less difficult but still very important problem of determining the stress intensity factors for cracks in laminates modeled as homogeneous solids. These papers provide the theoretical basis for valid reduction of experimental data. The last theoretical paper presents a fracture theory that can be used to explain the fracture behavior of laminates containing both circular and sharp notches.

The experimental papers present fracture toughness data on commonly used high-performance composites and adhesives. The first three papers present considerable data on the crack size effect observed in composites. The last paper presents a complete characterization of a structural adhesive used in bonding composites.

The two papers in the last section address the problem of providing a degree of damage tolerance in composite structures. This is achieved by designing in a crack arrestment mechanism into the structure so that a crack extending rapidly from service induced damage does not lead to structural failure.

G. P. Sendeckyj

Aerospace engineer, Structures Division, Air Force Flight Dynamics Laboratory, Wright-Patterson AFB, Ohio, symposium chairman.

1

P. D. Hilton[1] *and G. C. Sih*[1]

Three-Dimensional Analysis of Laminar Composites with Through Cracks

REFERENCE: Hilton, P. D. and Sih, G. C., **"Three-Dimensional Analysis of Laminar Composites with Through Cracks,"** *Fracture Mechanics of Composites, ASTM STP 593,* American Society for Testing and Materials, 1975, pp. 3–35.

ABSTRACT: The variational principle of minimum complementary potential energy is employed to develop an approximate three dimensional model for the stress distribution in laminar composites. This approximate theory is applied to the problem of a symmetric composite plate containing a through crack subjected to in-plane loading. Asymptotic solutions are obtained for the stress components in the vicinity of the leading crack edge. These solutions are in complete agreement with information obtained from an exact three-dimensional asymptotic analysis; that is, the in-plane variation of the stress components within each layer is described by the singular portion of the elastic, plane-strain crack solution. However, because of the three-dimensional character of the problem, the amplitude of the singular solution for the stress components varies along the leading crack edge. A two-parameter model incorporating the concept of surface and interfacial boundary layers is used to describe this transverse variation.

Results from the modeling and analysis performed here include a description of the through-the-thickness variation of the near-tip stress field, which has already proven to be of use in conjunction with photoelastic measurements, and an average or effective stress intensity factor for finite thickness homogeneous plates and laminates.

KEY WORDS: fracture properties, composite materials, stresses, laminates, crack propagation

This report describes research in the area of mathematical modeling for the behavior of laminated plates containing cracks through one or more layers and subjected to in-plane loading. Generally, laminates are composed of a series of individual layers which themselves contain uniaxial fibers and have corresponding preferred directions. As a result of the rather complicated structure of laminar composites, a number of different failure modes are possible. These mechanisms include fiber-matrix de-

---

[1] Associate professor and professor of Mechanics, respectively, Institute of Fracture and Solid Mechanics, Lehigh University, Bethlehem, Pa. 18015.

bonding within individual layers, delamination or separation of the layers, and the propagation of cracks through one or more layers. Primary consideration in this work is directed to the fracture mode of failure, and its possible interaction with the delamination process.

Testing procedures for single-phase materials to evaluate fracture toughness involve tension specimens with through cracks. The specimens are loaded to failure, and unstable crack propagation is observed. Similar testing procedures have recently been applied to composite specimens. Because of the more complicated structure of the "material," crack propagation can not be easily observed. In some cases, as previously reported [1],[2] the specimen is found to debond prior to failure, that is, separating into two halves. Thus, the conditions under which test results can be employed to predict apparent fracture toughness for composite materials is not completely understood. The results to be presented in this paper will lead to some consistent interpretations for fracture toughness of laminar plates and a description of rational methods for applying fracture mechanics to these composite materials.

It is recognized at the outset that the development and use of a mathematical model accounting for the detailed structure of a laminar composite is, for all practical purposes, impossible. Rather, a number of broad, simplifying assumptions are invoked to obtain an idealized model of the composite structure. Exact solutions to problems within the context of this model are still beyond the state of present knowledge. Thus, an approximate solution procedure is developed and applied to the idealized model to obtain some of the gross characteristics of laminates with through cracks.

It is assumed that the fiber and matrix components of an individual layer are sufficiently well adhered so that the overall behavior of the layer can be modeled by an equivalent homogeneous layer. The present calculations are for a symmetric laminate composed of three isotropic layers[3] which contains a through crack and is subjected to tensile loads. Even in this simplified model, it is clear that there will be a significant variation of the stress field in the thickness direction if the material properties of the individual layers are substantially different. Thus, the two-dimensional idealizations of generalized plane stress or plane strain are not applicable.

The regions around the crack edge are of primary interest in this problem as subsequent damage is most likely to occur in these regions. Hartranft and Sih [2] have demonstrated that for tensile loading normal to the crack direction the solution in the immediate vicinity of the crack edge must be of the form

---

[2] The italic numbers in brackets refer to the list of references appended to this paper.
[3] The formulation developed here is directly applicable to an n-layered symmetric laminate. The value $n = 3$ is used as an example.

$$\sigma_x = \frac{k(z)}{\sqrt{2r}}\left[\cos\left(\frac{\theta}{2}\right) + \frac{1}{2}\sin(\theta)\sin\left(\frac{3\theta}{2}\right)\right] + 0(1)$$

$$\sigma_y = \frac{k(z)}{\sqrt{2r}}\left[\cos\left(\frac{\theta}{2}\right) - \frac{1}{2}\sin(\theta)\sin\left(\frac{3\theta}{2}\right)\right] + 0(1)$$

$$\sigma_z = \nu(\sigma_x + \sigma_y) \tag{1}$$

$$\tau_{xy} = \frac{k(z)}{\sqrt{2r}}\left[\frac{1}{2}\sin\theta\cos\left(\frac{3\theta}{2}\right)\right] + 0(1)$$

$$\tau_{xz}, \tau_{yz} = 0(1) \quad \text{as} \quad r \to 0$$

except at points asymptotically close to the free surfaces and material interfaces. Here, (r, θ, z) is a local cylindrical coordinate system with z measured along the leading crack edge. Hartranft and Sih [3] have also developed an approximate, three-dimensional solution for finite thickness homogeneous plates containing through cracks which (1) agrees with Eq 1 and (2) gives information about $k(z)$, that is, the through-the-thickness variation of the near-tip stress field. This approximate solution is determined by assuming a form for the stress field which satisfies the equilibrium conditions and applying the variational principle of minimum complementary potential energy for determining the "best" solution of the chosen form. The plane-strain condition $\sigma_z = \nu(\sigma_x + \sigma_y)$, known from the exact solution, is used to determine $k(z)$, Eq 1, in the interior. A boundary layer is introduced to enable satisfaction of the free-surface conditions at $z = \pm h/2$, where h is the plate thickness.

An extension of this approximate, three-dimensional theory for finite thickness plates subjected to in-plane loads to problems involving laminated plates was presented by the authors in Ref 4. That model, employing a slightly different type of surface layer than the one used by Hartranft and Sih[4] and satisfying all the equilibrium equations and traction boundary conditions exactly, gives results concerning the gross (average through-the-thickness) influences of the geometric and material properties of the individual layers on the amplitude of the near-tip solution. On the other hand, that approximate solution did not properly describe the variation of the stress field in the vicinity of the crack tip with the through-the-thickness coordinate, z; that is, the shape of the curve for $k(z)$ was not significantly influenced by the material properties of the layers. The reason for this is believed to be closely associated with the use of the complementary energy principle which does not require satisfaction of displace-

_____

[4]The Hartranft-Sih boundary layer theory will be discussed further in connection with the condition of equilibrium.

ment continuity conditions. In the improved model to be presented here, interfacial boundary layers are included in addition to the free-surface layers. The interfacial layer is employed to introduce a constraint on the relative deformation of the two adjacent layers. The resulting solutions do indeed give a more realistic through-the-thickness distribution of the near-tip stress field.

An Approximate Three-Dimensional Theory for Laminates

In this section, the model previously developed for laminates in Ref 4 is reviewed briefly for completeness. The basis for this formulation is the variational principle of minimum complementary potential energy. It states that out of the set of all stress fields satisfying the equilibrium equations and traction boundary conditions, the exact solution minimizes the complementary energy. Further, if an approximate form is assumed for the stress field and all equilibrium conditions are enforced, then the stress field of that form which is closest to the exact solution in a mean square sense is found by minimizing the complementary potential energy with respect to the unknown functions in this assumed solution.

The assumed form of the stress components for the ith layer of the laminate has been chosen as a product of a function of the transverse variable, z, multiplied by a function of the in-plane variables, x and y, that is

$$\sigma_{ij}^{(i)} = f_{ij}^{(i)}(z)g_{ij}^{(i)}(x, y) \tag{2}$$

Solutions of this form which satisfy the equilibrium equations

$$\sum_{j=i}^{3} \frac{\partial \sigma_{ij}}{\partial x_j} = 0$$

can be written as

$$\sigma_z^{(i)} = f_i(z)Z_z^{(i)}(x, y)$$

$$[\tau_{xz}^{(i)}, \tau_{yz}^{(i)}] = -f_i'(z)[Z_x^{(i)}(x, y), Z_y^{(i)}(x, y)] \tag{3}$$

$$[\sigma_x^{(i)}, \sigma_y^{(i)}, \tau_{xy}^{(i)}] = f_i''(z)[S_x^{(i)}(x, y), S_y^{(i)}(x, y), T_{xy}^{(i)}(x, y)]$$

where

$$\frac{\partial S^{(i)}}{\partial x} + \frac{\partial T_{xy}^{(i)}}{\partial y} - Z_x^{(i)} = 0$$

$$\frac{\partial T_{xy}{}^{(i)}}{\partial x} + \frac{\partial S_y{}^{(i)}}{\partial y} - Z_y{}^{(i)} = 0 \qquad (4)$$

$$\frac{\partial Z_x{}^{(i)}}{\partial x} + \frac{\partial Z_y{}^{(i)}}{\partial y} - Z_z{}^{(i)} = 0$$

The traction continuity conditions between layers are satisfied by taking

$$[Z_x{}^{(i)}, Z_y{}^{(i)}, Z_z{}^{(i)}] = [Z_x, Z_y, Z_z]$$

and

$$f_i(z) = f_{i+1}(z)$$

$$f_i'(z) = f'_{i+1}(z)$$

at the value of z corresponding to the interface between layers i and $i + 1$.

A slightly more restricted form of this stress field is chosen for the present model in order to simplify the subsequent analysis, that is, the additional assumptions

$$[S_x{}^{(i)}, S_y{}^{(i)}, T_{xy}{}^{(i)}] = [S_x, S_y, T_{xy}]$$

are incorporated. The final form of the assumed stress field is

$$\sigma_z{}^{(i)} = f(z)Z_z(x, y)$$

$$[\tau_{xz}{}^{(i)}, \tau_{yz}{}^{(i)}] = -f'(z)[Z_x(x, y), Z_y(x, y)] \qquad (5)$$

$$[\sigma_x{}^{(i)}, \sigma_y{}^{(i)}, \tau_{xy}{}^{(i)}] = f''(z)[S_x(x, y), S_y(x, y), T_{xy}(x, y)]$$

with the conditions

$$\frac{\partial S_x}{\partial x} + \frac{\partial T_{xy}}{\partial y} - Z_x = 0$$

$$\frac{\partial T_{xy}}{\partial x} + \frac{\partial S_y}{\partial y} - Z_y = 0 \qquad (6)$$

$$\frac{\partial Z_x}{\partial x} + \frac{\partial Z_y}{\partial y} - Z_z = 0$$

and $f(z)$, $f'(z)$ must be continuous across the material interfaces ($f''(z)$ need not be continuous at these points).

This choice for the form of the stress components is, in part, motivated by the knowledge of the asymptotic near-tip solution for crack problems,

Eq 1. In the vicinity of the crack tip, the dependence of the stress components on the in-plane variables x and y must be of the same form within each layer. The reduction of the chosen form of the stress field from Eq 3 to Eq 5 enforces this result.

The laminate to be considered in the present calculations is composed of n layers whose material properties and geometry are chosen to maintain symmetry of the composite plate about the mid-plane, $z = 0$, see Fig. 1. The surfaces of the laminate are assumed to be traction free. Thus $f(\pm h/2) = f'(\pm h/2) = 0$.

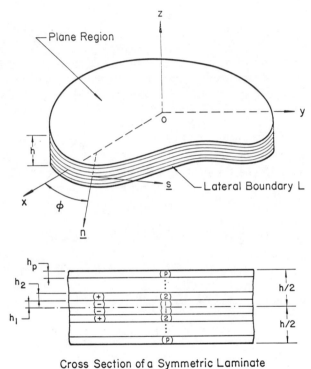

Cross Section of a Symmetric Laminate

FIG. 1—*An* n-*layered symmetric composite plate.*

In order to determine the equations which govern the choice of the unknown factors $(S_x, S_y, T_{xy}, Z_x, Z_y, Z_z)$ in the assumed stress field, the complementary potential energy is calculated and minimized with respect to these functions subject to the restraint conditions, Eq 6. This procedure leads to the set of governing equations:

$$I_1S_x + I_2S_y + I_4Z_z + \lambda_{1,x} = 0$$

$$I_1 S_y + I_2 S_x + I_4 Z_z + \lambda_{2,y} = 0$$

$$2(I_1 - I_2)T_{xy} + \lambda_{1,y} + \lambda_{2,x} = 0$$

$$I_3 Z_x + \lambda_1 + \lambda_{3,x} = 0$$

$$I_3 Z_y + \lambda_2 + \lambda_{3,y} = 0 \tag{7}$$

$$I_4(S_x + S_y) + I_5 Z_z + \lambda_3 = 0$$

$$Z_x = Z_{x,x} + Z_{y,y}$$

$$Z_x = S_{x,x} + T_{xy,y}$$

$$Z_y = T_{xy,x} + S_{y,y}$$

where λ_1, λ_2, and λ_3 are Lagrange multipliers used in the minimization process, see Ref 4 for details. The coefficients $I_1, \ldots I_5$ and the quantities u_x, u_y, u_z are given by:

$$I_1 = \sum_i \frac{1}{E_{(i)}} \int_{t_{i-1}}^{t_i} f''^2(z)dz$$

$$I_2 = -\sum_i \frac{\nu_{(i)}}{E_{(i)}} \int_{t_{i-1}}^{t_i} f''^2(z)dz$$

$$I_3 = \sum_i \frac{2(1+\nu_{(i)})}{E_{(i)}} \int_{t_{i-1}}^{t_i} f'^2(z)dz$$

$$I_4 = -\sum_i \frac{\nu_{(i)}}{E_{(i)}} \int_{t_{i-1}}^{t_i} f(z)f''(z)dz$$

$$I_5 = \sum_i \frac{1}{E_{(i)}} \int_{t_{i-1}}^{t_i} f^2(z)dz \tag{8}$$

$$u_x = \sum_i \int_{t_{i-1}}^{t_i} \bar{U}_x^{(i)} f''(z)dz$$

$$u_y = \sum_i \int_{t_{i-1}}^{t_i} \bar{U}_y^{(i)} f''(z)dz$$

$$u_z = -\sum_i \int_{t_{i-1}}^{t_i} \bar{U}_z^{(i)} f'(z)dz$$

The boundary conditions associated with the in-plane variables S_x, S_y, ... can be of the traction or displacement type; that is, on the contour c along the plate edge one can prescribe either the equivalent normal traction $S_n = \overline{S}_n$ or the corresponding averaged displacement component $\lambda_n = -\overline{u}_n$, the equivalent inplane, tangential traction $T_{ns} = \overline{T}_{ns}$ as averaged displacement component $\lambda_s = -\overline{u}_s$, and the equivalent transverse traction $Z_n = \overline{Z}_n$ as averaged displacement component $\lambda_3 = -\overline{u}_z$.

A Laminar Plate Containing a Through Crack Subjected to Tensile Loading

For this analysis, the crack length is taken as small in comparison with the in-plate dimensions of the plate. The stress field in the vicinity of the crack is thus independent of local boundary effects, and the plate can be modeled as infinite in the two in-plane directions. This assumption simplifies the analysis significantly while maintaining the essential characteristics of the crack laminar plate problem.

In particular, the problem of a laminar plate containing a crack in a uniaxial far-field stress state will be considered. The crack is directed normal to the loading direction, thus modeling the most damaging type of flaw. This problem can be expressed as the superposition of two auxiliary problems. The first auxiliary problem is that of an uncracked plate subjected to the same loading conditions as the actual cracked plate. For the second auxiliary problem, the cracked plate configuration is considered with no boundary loads. Instead, the crack faces are loaded with tractions of equal magnitude but opposite sense to those found at the crack location in the first problem. Thus, the superposition of the two problems yields the cracked plate with traction-free crack faces and remote loading as originally described.

The first of the auxiliary problems, an uncracked plate in a far, uniform stress field, has nonsingular stress components and as such does not contribute to the crack-tip singularity. Therefore, the stress field in the vicinity of the crack tips for the case of crack face loading is identical to that for the remote loading situation of the actual cracked plate. It is mathematically advantageous to consider the crack face loading problem because it leads to stress fields which die out far from the crack and can thus be treated by transform techniques.

The plate geometry is shown in Fig. 2 for the special case of a three-layer composite. Consider the region x, y, $z > 0$. The boundary and symmetric conditions from three-dimensional elasticity are:

on $y = 0$

$$\tau_{xy} = \tau_{yz} = 0$$

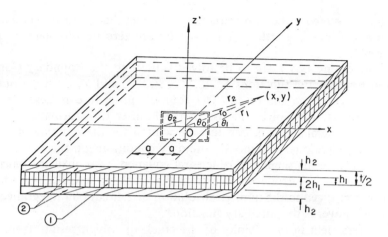

FIG. 2—*A three-layered plate containing a through crack.*

$$\sigma_y = p(x, z), \qquad 0 \leqslant x \leqslant a$$

$$u_y = 0, x > a \tag{9}$$

on $x = 0$

$$\tau_{xy} = \tau_{xz} = 0$$

$$u_x = 0$$

and on $z = 0$

$$\tau_{xz} = \tau_{yz} = 0$$

$$u_z = 0$$

The equivalent boundary conditions for the approximate theory are:
on $y = 0$

$$T_{xy} = Z_y = 0$$

$$S_y = P(x), \qquad 0 \leqslant x \leqslant a \tag{10}$$

$$\lambda_2 = 0, x > a$$

on $x = 0$

$$T_{xy} = Z_x = 0$$

$$\lambda_1 = 0$$

and $f(z)$ is required to be symmetric in z to model the symmetry conditions on the $z = 0$ plane. Further, $f(z)$ and $f'(z)$ are zero on the plate surface $z = \pm h/2$.

The governing Eqs 7 are to be solved subject to the Boundary Conditions 9. Further, the functions S_x, S_y, T_{xy}, Z_x, Z_y, and Z_z must die out at large distances from the crack. The solution procedure is described in detail in Ref 4. It involves the use of the Fourier transformation in the x-variable. General solutions can then be written for the resulting ordinary differential equations. The mixed boundary conditions on the $y = z = 0$ axis lead to a set of singular dual-integral equations. An auxiliary function $\psi(s)$, $0 \leqslant s \leqslant 1$ is introduced to extract the crack tip singularity and the problem is reduced to the numerical solution of a Fredholm integral equation which governs this auxiliary function.

The stress field in the vicinity of the crack tip which results from the solution procedure can be expressed in the form:

$$\sigma_x = \frac{K\sigma_p(z)\sqrt{a}}{\sqrt{2r_1}}\left[\cos\left(\frac{\theta_1}{2}\right) - \tfrac{1}{2}\sin(\theta_1)\sin\left(\frac{3\theta_1}{2}\right)\right] + 0(1)$$

$$\sigma_y = \frac{K\sigma_p(z)\sqrt{a}}{\sqrt{2r_1}}\left[\cos\left(\frac{\theta_1}{2}\right) + \tfrac{1}{2}\sin(\theta_1)\sin\left(\frac{3\theta_1}{2}\right)\right] + 0(1)$$

$$\tau_{xy} = \frac{K\sigma_p(z)\sqrt{a}}{\sqrt{2r_1}}\left[\tfrac{1}{2}\sin(\theta_1)\cos\left(\frac{3\theta_1}{2}\right)\right] + 0(1) \tag{11}$$

$$\sigma_z = \frac{K\sigma_T(z)\sqrt{a}}{\sqrt{2r_1}}\left[\cos\left(\frac{\theta_1}{2}\right)\right] + 0(1)$$

$$\tau_{xy} = \tau_{yz} = 0(1)$$

where

$$K = a\Psi(1)C_1,$$
$$\sigma_p(z) = Pf''(z), \text{ and}$$
$$\sigma_T(z) = C_2Pf(z).$$

for the local cylindrical coordinate system (r_1, θ_1, z) with z measured along the leading crack edge. The constants C_1 and C_2 are given in Ref 4. Note that the stress field in the vicinity of the crack tip, as just given, contains the usual square root singularity in the plane normal to the crack front. The dependence of the stress components on the in-plane variables (r_1, θ_1) obtained here is in complete agreement with the exact three-dimensional solution for a crack in an elastic medium [2]. The dependence of the near-tip stress field on the through-the-thickness coordinate, z, will be discussed in the following section.

Dependence of the Near-Tip Stress Field on the Transverse Coordinate z

The function $f(z)$ is to be chosen so as to most accurately approximate or model the z-dependence of the near-tip stress field. It is known, from exact asymptotic analysis [2] discussed earlier, that within the ith layer the singular portions of the normal stress components are related by the equation

$$\sigma_z = \nu_i(\sigma_x + \sigma_y) \tag{12}$$

This condition, often referred to as plane strain, is employed to determine the function $f(z)$ in the interior of each layer. Substitution of the near tip solution, Eq 11, into Eq 12, gives

$$f_i''(z) + p_i^2 f_i(z) = 0 \tag{13}$$

where

$$p_i^2 = -(C_2/2\nu_i)$$

The general solution to these equations does not possess sufficient free parameters to satisfy the traction-free surface conditions ($f = f' = 0$). This result is not unexpected as the exact three-dimensional analysis demonstrates that the plane strain condition, Eq 12, must hold in the interior of the body but may be violated in the immediate vicinity of the free surfaces [2]. There is experimental evidence to suggest that the stress field should be qualitatively different from the interior solution over a thin layer at the free surface. Fractured test specimens are observed to possess "shear lips," thin surface layers in which the material behavior is clearly distinct from that in the specimen interior.

In the Hartranft-Sih [3] approximate solution for a homogeneous specimen containing a through crack, a boundary layer has been introduced at the free surface in order to (1) satisfy the mathematical conditions of surface $f = f' = 0$ and (2) model the experimentally observed character of the near-tip behavior. Within that boundary layer separate polynomial expressions were employed to connect the respective functions $f(z)$ and $f'(z)$ to zero at the free surface. As no special condition is required on $f''(z)$ at the surface, the trigonometric solution to Eq 13 for $f''(z)$ was carried through the boundary layer. The solution developed in this manner violates some of the equilibrium conditions within the boundary layer.[5] It does, however, result in a model for the z-variation of the stress field which can be chosen to match experimental observations. Related experimental work has been carried out [5, 6] which confirms the usefulness of the Hartranft-Sih model.

---

[5] The continuum concept and related model of the actual material must break down for lengths which are not significantly larger than the characteristic lengths of the material structures, for example, grain size. Thus, the continuum analysis cannot properly predict surface phenomena for real materials.

In the previously reported [4] extension of the Hartranft-Sih approximate solution procedure to laminates, a different type of surface layer than that just described was introduced. A higher order polynomial expression was chosen to represent the function $f(z)$ in this layer and the first and second derivatives of this function were used to represent the quantities $f'(z)$ and $f''(z)$, respectively. The coefficients for the polynomial expression were chosen so as to enforce (1) continuity of f, f', and f'' at the surface where the boundary layer solution was connected to the interior solution and (2) the conditions $f = f' = 0$ at the free surface. It was found that, with this model, the boundary layer solution has a dominating effect on the coefficients of the governing equations $I_1, \ldots I_5$ (see Eq 8). For example, in the special case $\nu_1 = \nu_2$, the interior solutions as obtained from Eq 13 is

$$f(z) = \cos p_1 z$$

and the only admissible value for p_1 is found to be approximately equal to

$$\frac{\pi/2}{(h_1 + h_2)}.$$

Thus, the function of $f(z)(-h_1 - h_2 < z < h_1 + h_2)$ has the appearance of the cosine curve for $(-90° < 0 < 90°)$. This solution, while satisfying all the equilibrium conditions, describes the z-variation of the near-tip stress field only in an approximate manner. It does not predict the "shear-lip" phenomenon. Moreover, the reason that this solution can only be considered as approximate is because of the application of the complementary potential energy principle. Recall, the principle requires satisfaction of equilibrium conditions but does not demand imposition of any conditions on the displacement field. Examination of the reported solution [4] indicates a discontinuity of in-plane strains across the material interfaces.

In the present formulation an attempt is made to constrain the relative deformation for the various layers of the composite plate. As discussed earlier, the plane-strain condition $\sigma_z = \nu_i(\sigma_x + \sigma_y)$ need not be satisfied in the vicinity of the material interfaces. This suggests the introduction of a transition layer to connect the interior, plane-strain solutions for adjacent layers. The same type of difficulties mentioned in conjunction with the development of a free-surface boundary layer arise again, for example, the application of a continuum model for the interfacial surfaces is questionable. Yet the interior solutions must be connected across this region. The attitude to be adopted at this time is to choose the transition layer description in such a way so that it has minimum influence on the character of the overall solution.[6] Rather than complete satisfaction of the equilibrium conditions within the free-surface and interfacial-transition layers, emphasis

---

[6] A careful boundary layer type analysis is recommended for future work.

will be put on modeling of the z-variation of the near-tip stress field. This approach suggests choices for the functions $f'(z)$ and $f''(z)$ in the boundary layers which result in small contributions to the coefficients of the governing equations, $I_1, \ldots I_5$. To accomplish this, the Hartranft-Sih approach discussed earlier is employed to describe the z-variation of the near-tip stress field in these thin strips.

The present model for the z-distribution of the near-tip stress field for a three-layer composite[7] is developed in the following manner. The plane-strain conditions, Eq 12, are enforced in the interior of each layer of the composite plate. A boundary layer of thickness ε_o is introduced at the free surface, and an interfacial-transition layer of thickness $\varepsilon_1 + \varepsilon_2$ is employed to connect the plane-strain solutions across the material interface (Fig. 3). The general solution to Eq. 13 for the plane-strain condition,

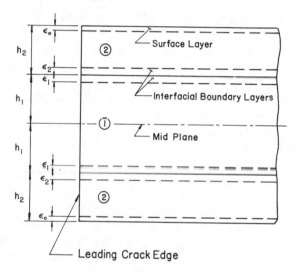

FIG. 3—*The model for the z-dependence of the near-tip stress field (plate cross section).*

which satisfies the symmetry properties of this problem can be expressed as:

$$f_1(z) = \cos p_1 z, \quad -h_1 + \varepsilon_1 < z < h_1 - \varepsilon_1$$

$$f_2(z) = A \sin p_2(z - h_1 - h_2 \pm a), \qquad h_1 + \varepsilon_2 < z < h_1 + h_2 - \varepsilon_0 \tag{14}$$

The amplitude of $f_1(z)$ can be arbitrarily chosen as 1.0 without loss of

---

[7] Detailed analysis and numerical calculations have been carried out for the three-layer composite system; however, the modeling approach described here is applicable to n-layer symmetric composites.

generality because of the product form assumed for the stress field, Eq 5. The eigenvalues p_1 and p_2 are given by Eq 13.

Attention is now directed to the region in the vicinity of the traction-free surface ($z = h_1 + h_2$). The transverse normal and shear stress components (σ_z, τ_{xz}, and τ_{yz}) are required to approach zero at this surface. Thus, their coefficients $f(z)$ and $f'(z)$ are specified as zero at $z = h_1 + h_2$. No similar condition exists for the coefficient of the in-plane stress components, $f''(z)$. In order to satisfy these conditions, separate polynomial expressions $g_1(z)$ and $g_2(z)$ are introduced to connect the interior solutions for $f(z)$ and $f'(z)$, respectively, through the boundary layer, to zero at the free surface, that is

$$g_1(z) = e_1(z - h_1 - h_2)^3 + e_2(z - h_1 - h_2)^2$$

$$g_2(z) = b_1(z - h_1 - h_2)^2 + b_2(z - h_1 - h_2)$$

(15)

The coefficients e_1 and e_2 are chosen so that $g_1(z)$ and its first derivative are the continuation of the interior solution ($f_2(z) = A \sin p_2(z - h_1 - h_2 - \alpha)$) at $z = h_1 + h_2 - \varepsilon_0$. Similarly, the coefficients b_1 and b_2 are determined from the requirement that $g_2(z)$ and its slope match the first and second derivatives of the interior solution at $z = h_1 + h_2 - \varepsilon_0$, respectively. The interior solution for the function $f''(z)(f''(z) = -p_2 A \sin p_2 (z - h_1 - h_2))$ is simply continued through the boundary layer as the z-variation of the in-plane stress components.

Consider the material interface next. The traction continuity conditions across this interface require that $f(z)$ and $f'(z)$ vary continuously from one layer to the next. Again, the equilibrium requirements of the complementary potential energy approach make no special demands on the coefficient of the in-plane stress components, $f''(z)$, across this interface. The function $f''(z)$ will be employed in this formulation as a mechanism to couple the deformation fields in the adjacent layers. Enforcement of complete continuity of displacement components across the interface will not in general be possible with the present formulation. However, in the special case for which the Poisson's ratios for the adjacent layers are the same ($\nu_1 = \nu_2$), the displacement field across the interface becomes exactly continuous when the condition

$$\frac{f''_1(h_1)}{\mu_1} = \frac{f''_2(h_1)}{\mu_2}$$

(16)

is imposed, where μ_i is the shear modulus of the ith layer. For $\nu_1 \neq \nu_2$, Eq 16 still enforces continuity of the transverse shearing strains and offers a reasonable approximation to continuity conditions on the in-plane normal strain components. This condition, Eq 16, will be employed to relate the deformations in the adjacent layers with the recognization that is exact only in the special case $v_1 = v_2$.

The transition layer is treated in a manner similar to that just described for the surface layer. Polynomial expressions $g_3(z)$ and $g_4(z)$ are introduced as the extensions of the functions $f(z)$ and $f'(z)$ in the transition layer, respectively, that is

$$g_3(z) = c_1 z^4 + c_2 z^3 + c_3 z + c_4$$

$$g_4(z) = d_1 z^4 + d_2 z^3 + d_3 z + d_4, \quad h_1 - \varepsilon_1 \leqslant z \leqslant h_1 + \varepsilon_2 \tag{17}$$

where $c_1, \ldots c_4$ are obtained from the continuity conditions on $g_3(z)$ and $g_3'(z)$ at $z = h_1 - \varepsilon_1$ and $h_1 + \varepsilon_2$. The coefficients $d_1, \ldots d_4$ are found so that $g_4(z)$ and $g_4'(z)$ match the corresponding interior solutions for the adjacent layers. The coefficient of the in-plane stress components is chosen as

$$f''(z) = \begin{cases} -p_1^2 \cos p_1 z, & h_1 - \varepsilon_1 < z < h_1 \\ \\ -A p_2^2 \sin p_2 (z - h_1 - h_2 - \alpha), & h_1 < z < h_1 + \varepsilon_2 \end{cases} \tag{18}$$

and the constant A is determined from Eq 16 as

$$A = -\frac{\mu_2 p_1^2}{\mu_1 p_2^2} \frac{\cos p_1 h_1}{\sin p_2 (h_2 + \alpha)} \tag{19}$$

The phase angle α in the outer layer solution is arbitrary in the present formulation and may be chosen to match experimental results. For infinitely thin boundary layers ($\varepsilon_1 = \varepsilon_2 = \varepsilon_0 = 0$), the plane-strain condition (Eq 13) is satisfied exactly for all values of p_1 with $p_2^2 = v_1/v_2 p_1^2$. The boundary layer solutions have been chosen so that their influence on I_1, $\ldots I_5$ will be small for finite thickness boundary layers. Thin boundary layers thus lead to small errors in the satisfaction of Eq 13 which can be eliminated by introducing higher order terms to the polynomial solutions employed in these layers [3]. Such adjustments will not in any way affect the character of the resulting solutions and have not been included in the calculated results to be reported.[8]

---

[8] In carrying out these calculations, the values for p_i were chosen and the corresponding functions $f(z)$ were determined. The constant C_2 in Eq 13 ($p_i^2 = -C_2/2v_i$) was then calculated and a new value for p_i was determined from this equation. The new value for p_i never differed from the initial choice by more than 2 percent in the calculations performed.

Numerical Results

The present approximate formulation for the problem of a three-layered composite plate containing a through crack subjected to pressure loading on its surfaces takes into account the following geometric and material properties of the laminate: h_1/a, h_2/h_1, E_1/E_2, v_1, and v_2 (see Fig. 2). The stress components in the vicinity of the crack edge are given by Eq 11. Note that the amplitude of this near-tip stress field can be expressed as $k(z) = K\sigma_p(z)\sqrt{a}$ where $\sigma_p(z) = Pf_i''(z)$ is the crack loading distribution. The stress intensity factor $k(z)$ divided by the crack face loading distribution $\sigma_p(z)$ is equal to $K\sqrt{a}$. Thus, the single parameter K describes the influence of the geometric and material properties of the laminate on the near-tip stress field.

For a given composite it is possible to choose the parameters p_1 and α, as well as the boundary layer thicknesses ε_1, ε_2, and ε_0, which influence the through-the-thickness variation of the stress field (see Eqs 14 thru 19) to match experimental results. The stress intensification parameter K is then obtained from the numerical solution of a Fredholm integral equation in terms of the composite properties and the free parameters p_1, α, ε_1, ε_2, and ε_0.

The approximate model developed here for a laminate containing a through crack will first be applied to the special case of a homogeneous plate ($E_1/E_2 = 1.0$, $v_1 = v_2$) to enable comparison of this formulation with previously reported results. In the case of a homogeneous plate containing a through crack the transition layer in this formulation becomes artificial. Though the transition layer itself is allowed to remain in the analysis, the special relation $p_1(h_1 + h_2 + \alpha) = \pi/2$ is enforced so that the solution in the outer layers is the natural extension of that in the middle layer.

The influence of the choice for p_1 on the solution is demonstrated for the case $h_2/h_1 = 2.0$. The boundary layer thicknesses have been chosen as $\varepsilon_1 = \varepsilon_2 = \varepsilon_0 = 0.02\ h_1/a$. Numerical results for the stress intensification parameter K are given in Table 1 and the corresponding curves for $f(z)$ and $f'(z)$ are shown in Figs. 4 and 5. (These curves are independent of h_1/a). Recall the coefficient of the in-plane stress components $f''(z)$ is given by

TABLE 1—$E_1/E_2 = 1.0$, $h_2/h_1 = 2.0$, $h_1/a = 1.0$, $v_1 = v_2 = 0.3$, $\varepsilon_1 = \varepsilon_2 = \varepsilon_0 = 0.02$.

$p_1 h_1$	α/h_1	K
0.5236	0.0	0.8830
0.31416	2.0	0.8958
0.1047	12.0	0.9263

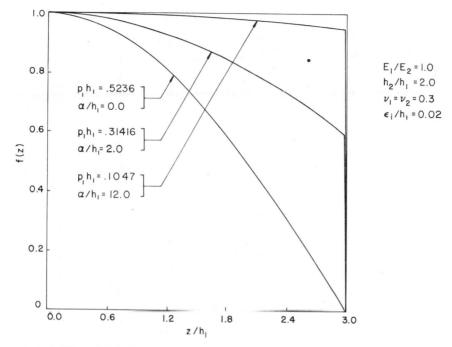

FIG. 4—The function f(z) which governs the transverse variation of the near-tip, normal-stress component.

$f''(z) = -p_i^2 f(z)$ except in the boundary layers where it has a discontinuity; thus, no separate curves for this function are included.

The results indicate that for a given h_1/a, the parameter K increases with decreasing values of p_1. The corresponding curves for $f(z)$ become flatter indicating that the interior solution is approaching the plane-strain result for which K is 1.0. The stress intensification parameter K is then plotted against $h_1/a = h/3a$ in Fig. 6. This graph has the same character observed by other authors [3,4], that is, K increases monotonically toward the plane-strain result ($K = 1.0$) with increasing plate thickness.

For the next example, we consider the case in which the middle layer of the composite is stiffer than the outside layers. It is necessary to choose a range of reasonable values for the parameters p_1, α, ε_1, ε_2, and ε_0 in order to model the anticipated z-variation of the near-tip stress field. In this case, the in-plane stresses are expected to be maximum at the mid-plane of the plate and to decrease monotonically with increasing z. For this situation to exist, it is necessary that $p_1 < \pi/2h_1$ and $p_2(h_2 + \alpha) < \pi/2$. For purposes of illustration we take the example: $h_2/h_1 = 2.0$, $E_1/E_2 = 10.0$, $\nu_1 = \nu_2 = 0.3$.

Calculations are performed for a number of choices for p_1 and α within the range just suggested, at various values of h_1/a. The resulting functions

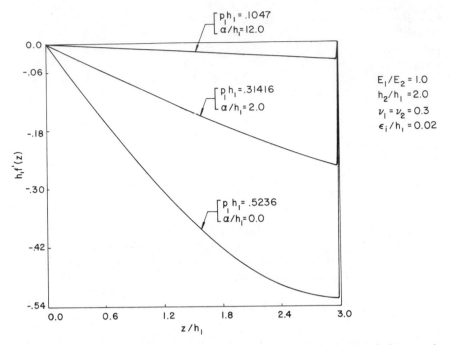

FIG. 5—*The function* $f'(z)$ *which describes the transverse variation of the near-tip, anti-plane shearing stress components.*

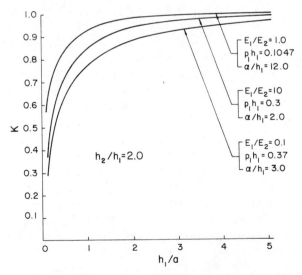

FIG. 6—*The stress intensification parameter K as a function of* h_1/a *for a composite plate.*

$f(z)$ and $f'(z)$ are shown in Figs. 7 and 8 and the corresponding stress intensification factors are given in Table 2. The first six sets of results given in the table indicate the effect of the choices for p_1 and α on the stress intensification parameter K. Note that K is rather sensitive to the choice of the z-variation of the near-tip stress field. This indicates a strong coupling of the in-plane and transverse character of the stress field in the vicinity of the crack tip.

By comparing the fourth and tenth sets of results, one can see that K is not significantly influenced by the boundary layer thicknesses $(\varepsilon_1, \varepsilon_2, \varepsilon_0)$. Recall, the boundary layer solutions were purposely chosen to achieve this effect.

The results presented in rows seven through twelve of Table 2 demonstrate the dependence of K on the relative crack length for a given choice of the parameters p_1, α, ε_1, ε_2, and ε_0. Here h_2/h_1 is fixed at 2.0 and values of K are given for various values of h_1/a between 0.1 and 5.0. As observed for the homogeneous plate discussed earlier, it is seen here that K increases with decreasing crack length approaching the plane-strain result ($K = 1.0$) asymptotically.

The influence of relative layer height, h_2/h_1, on K is demonstrated in this table; compare data sets 1 thru 6 ($h_1/h_2 = 2.0$) with 13 thru 18 ($h_1/$

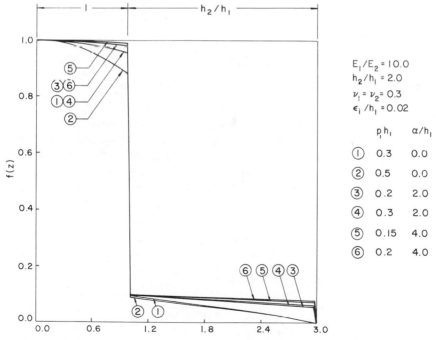

FIG. 7—The function f(z) which governs the transverse variation of the near-tip, normal-stress component.

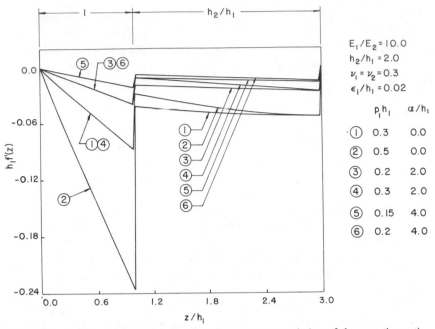

FIG. 8—*The function* f′ (z) *which describes the transverse variation of the near-tip, anti-plane shearing stress components.*

$h_2 = 1.0$) and 19 thru 24 ($h_1/h_2 = 5.0$. The functions $f(z)$ and $f'(z)$ corresponding to these data sets are shown graphically in Figs. 9 thru 12. The general trend to be observed is that for fixed h_1/a, K increases with increasing h_2/h_1.

Some examples in which the outer layers of the composite are stiffer than the middle layer ($E_1/E_2 = 0.1$) are considered next. For these situations, the stress level is expected to be higher in the outer layers than in the central layer. Thus, $f(z)$ should have a peak (maximum) within the outer layer. The choices for the parameters p_1 and α which govern the z-variation of the near-tip stress field are based on the expected character of the solution as previously discussed. This suggests the following conditions:

$$p_1h_1 < \frac{\pi}{2}, \ p_2\alpha < \frac{\pi}{2}, \qquad p_2(h_2 + \alpha) > \frac{\pi}{2}$$

where

$$p_2 = \sqrt{\frac{\nu_1}{\nu_2}} p_1$$

Graphs of $f(z)$ and $f'(z)$ are exhibited in Figs. 13 and 14 for $h_2/h_1 = 2.0$

TABLE 2—$E_1/E_2 = 10.0$, $v_1 = v_2 = 0.3$.

	h_1/a	h_2/h_1	p_1h_1	α/h_1	$h_1\varepsilon_1$	$h_1\varepsilon_2$	$h_1\varepsilon_0$	K
1	1.0	2.0	0.3	0.0	0.02	0.02	0.02	0.9224
2	1.0	2.0	0.5	0.0	0.02	0.02	0.02	0.7975
3	1.0	2.0	0.2	2.0	0.02	0.02	0.02	0.9348
4	1.0	2.0	0.3	2.0	0.02	0.02	0.02	0.8457
5	1.0	2.0	0.15	4.0	0.02	0.02	0.02	0.9464
6	1.0	2.0	0.2	4.0	0.02	0.02	0.02	0.8860
7	0.1	2.0	0.3	2.0	0.1	0.1	0.1	0.3692
8	0.2	2.0	0.3	2.0	0.1	0.1	0.1	0.5098
9	0.5	2.0	0.3	2.0	0.1	0.1	0.1	0.7106
10	1.0	2.0	0.3	2.0	0.1	0.1	0.1	0.8469
11	2.0	2.0	0.3	2.0	0.1	0.1	0.1	0.9343
12	5.0	2.0	0.3	2.0	0.1	0.1	0.1	0.9832
13	1.0	1.0	0.8	0.0	0.1	0.1	0.1	0.7159
14	1.0	1.0	1.0	0.0	0.1	0.1	0.1	0.6784
15	1.0	1.0	0.35	2.0	0.1	0.1	0.1	0.8125
16	1.0	1.0	0.5	2.0	0.1	0.1	0.1	0.7453
17	1.0	1.0	0.2	4.0	0.1	0.1	0.1	0.8808
18	1.0	1.0	0.3	4.0	0.1	0.1	0.1	0.7904
19	1.0	5.0	0.25	0.0	0.1	0.1	0.1	0.9200
20	1.0	5.0	0.3	0.0	0.1	0.1	0.1	0.8856
21	1.0	5.0	0.20	1.0	0.1	0.1	0.1	0.9386
22	1.0	5.0	0.25	1.0	0.1	0.1	0.1	0.8991
23	1.0	5.0	0.15	2.0	0.1	0.1	0.1	0.9635
24	1.0	5.0	0.20	2.0	0.1	0.1	0.1	0.9223

and various values of p_1 and α in the range just suggested.[9] The corresponding values of the stress intensification parameter K are given in Table 3. Note that for a given composite, the particular choices for p_1 and α may result in values for K which differ by as much as 10 percent. The influence of relative layer height (h_2/h_1) is demonstrated by the results given in Table 3 for $h_2/h_1 = 1.0, 2.0, 5.0$ at various p_1 and α. The reasonable choices for p_1 and α (in the range suggested) do differ at different values of h_2/h_1. Thus, direct comparison of resulting K values may be deceptive. The general trend is again that increasing relative plate thickness (increasing h_2/h_1 at constant h_1/a) increases the stress intensification parameter.

Calculations to determine the influence of the Poisson's ratios of the layers on the stress intensification parameter K for the laminate have been carried out for the sample case $h_1/a = 1.0$, $h_2/h_1 = 2.0$ at relative layer stiffnesses of $E_1/E_2 = 0.1$ and 10.0. The boundary layer thicknesses, ε_1, ε_2, and ε_0, were taken as $0.1\ h_1$ for these calculations. Values of p_1 and α have been chosen from the set of results reported earlier for the special

[9] The choice of the general character of $f(z)$ discussed earlier (the plane-strain conditions) requires that $f(z)$ ($= \cos p_1 z$) decrease with increasing z in the middle layer of the composite. This characteristic of $f(z)$ is contrary to the author's intuition for situations where E_1/E_2 is less than 1.0. Further analysis as well as experimentation is needed to resolve this dilemma.

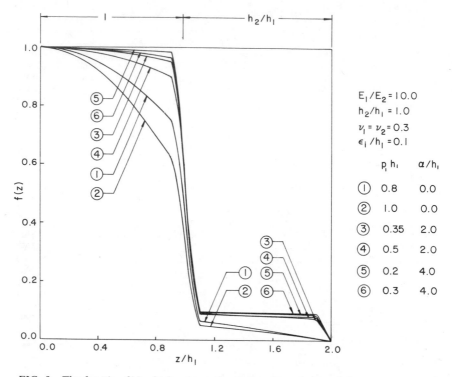

FIG. 9—*The function* f(z) *which governs the transverse variation of the near-tip, normal-stress component.*

case $v_1 = v_2 = 3$. The resulting K values are given in Table 4. Note that they are significantly influenced by the Poisson's ratios of the component materials making up the laminate. Some care is required in interpreting these results. Calculations have been performed for constant values of p_1 and α; thus the eigenvalue p_2 ($p_2 = p_1 \sqrt{v_1/v_2}$) which governs the behavior of the outer layers differs from one set of v_1, v_2 values to the next. As v_1/v_2 is increased, p_2 increases causing a corresponding increase in the rate of z-variation of the near-tip stress field in the outer layers of the composite. In previous results, it has been generally observed that the stress intensification parameter K decreases as the rate of change of the stress field with z increases. Equation 13 indicates that $f(z)$ will vary more quickly in the layers with the smaller Poisson's ratio. Again, some experimental work is needed to determine the appropriate values for p_1 and α in order to pin down these results.

Discussion of Results

The stress intensification parameter K is a measure of the averaged load transfer to the crack edge, that is, for a given crack face loading distribution

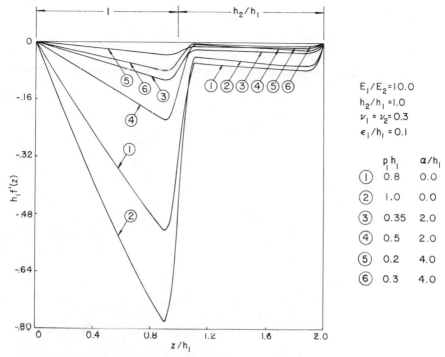

FIG. 10—*The function* $f'(z)$ *which describes the transverse variation of the near-tip, anti-plane shearing stress components.*

$\sigma^\circ = P f''(z)$, the corresponding z-variation of the near-tip stress field is $KP\sqrt{a}\, f''(z)$. Thus, K is a parameter, analogous to the stress intensity factor in two-dimensional fracture mechanics, for correlating fracture results.

The numerical results obtained here indicate a general trend: K increases asymptotically toward 1.0 with increasing specimen thickness to crack length ratio.

The actual values obtained for K associated with any particular set of geometric and material properties for the crack laminate were found to be significantly influenced by the choice of the modeling parameters p_1 and α. Proper choices for the present modeling approach will have to be determined experimentally. Some experimental work related to a similar model for homogeneous plates in bending has already been carried out [5] and pho-toelasticity techniques are currently being employed at Lehigh University to study the through-the-thickness variation of the stress field for tension specimens containing cracks. In general, it appears that p_1, which controls the rate at which $f(z)$ changes with z, should increase as the material prop-erties of the constituents composing the laminate become more dissimilar. This anticipated trend suggests that K will generally be lower for laminates

TABLE 3—$E_1/E_2 = 0.1$, $\nu_1 = \nu_2 = 0.3$.

	h_1/a	h_2/h_1	p_1h_1	α/h_1	$h_1\varepsilon_1$	$h_1\varepsilon_2$	$h_1\varepsilon_0$	K
1	1.0	2.0	0.8	0.0	0.02	0.02	0.02	0.7918
2	1.0	2.0	1.0	0.0	0.02	0.02	0.02	0.7094
3	1.0	2.0	0.45	2.0	0.02	0.02	0.02	0.7766
4	1.0	2.0	0.48	2.0	0.02	0.02	0.02	0.7537
5	1.0	2.0	0.35	3.0	0.02	0.02	0.02	0.7982
6	1.0	2.0	0.37	3.0	0.02	0.02	0.02	0.7764
7	0.1	2.0	0.37	3.0	0.1	0.1	0.1	0.3178
8	0.2	2.0	0.37	3.0	0.1	0.1	0.1	0.4528
9	0.5	2.0	0.37	3.0	0.1	0.1	0.1	0.6405
10	1.0	2.0	0.37	3.0	0.1	0.1	0.1	0.7709
11	2.0	2.0	0.37	3.0	0.1	0.1	0.1	0.8800
12	5.0	2.0	0.37	3.0	0.1	0.1	0.1	0.9630
13	1.0	1.0	0.8	1.2	0.1	0.1	0.1	0.6522
14	1.0	1.0	0.8	1.5	0.1	0.1	0.1	0.6360
15	1.0	1.0	0.4	3.0	0.1	0.1	0.1	0.7504
16	1.0	1.0	0.4	3.5	0.1	0.1	0.1	0.7151
17	1.0	1.0	0.2	7.0	0.1	0.1	0.1	0.7808
18	1.0	1.0	0.2	7.5	0.1	0.1	0.1	0.7583
19	1.0	5.0	0.4	0.0	0.1	0.1	0.1	0.8978
20	1.0	5.0	0.5	0.0	0.1	0.1	0.1	0.8634
21	1.0	5.0	0.4	1.0	0.1	0.1	0.1	0.8688
22	1.0	5.0	0.45	1.0	0.1	0.1	0.1	0.8607
23	1.0	5.0	0.24	3.0	0.1	0.1	0.1	0.9053
24	1.0	5.0	0.28	3.0	0.1	0.1	0.1	0.8821

TABLE 4—$h_1/a = 1.0$, $h_2/h_1 = 2.0$ ($\varepsilon_1 = \varepsilon_2 = \varepsilon_0 = 0.1$).

ν_1	ν_2	K
0.3	0.3	0.7709
0.25	0.35	0.8477
0.35	0.25	0.7774
0.3	0.3	0.8469
0.25	0.35	0.8788
0.35	0.25	0.8138

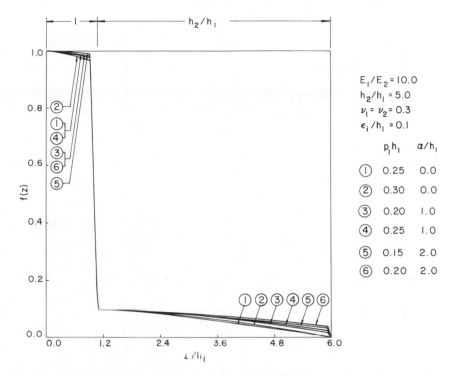

FIG. 11   *The function f(z) which governs the transverse variation of the near-tip, normal-stress component.*

than for corresponding single-phase plates and that "apparent fracture toughness" may be increased by lamination.

According to the approximate calculations performed here, the transverse shearing stresses will be nonsingular in the vicinity of the leading crack edge for laminated plates subjected to tensile loading.

Let us look in more detail at the distribution of the singular stress components along the crack edge. Recall, both the approximate formulation developed here and the exact three-dimensional asymptotic solution predict that the in-plane stress components within each layer will have the same form as the two-dimensional plane-strain result except that the "stress intensity factor" will depend on z, that is

$$\sigma_{ij} = \frac{k(z)}{\sqrt{2r}} \, g_{ij}(\theta), \quad i, j = 1, 2$$

where (r, θ, z) are local cylindrical coordinates centered on the crack edge. Further, the singular portion of the transverse normal stress component σ_z is equal to $\nu_1(\sigma_x + \sigma_y)$. In the present model the stress intensity factor

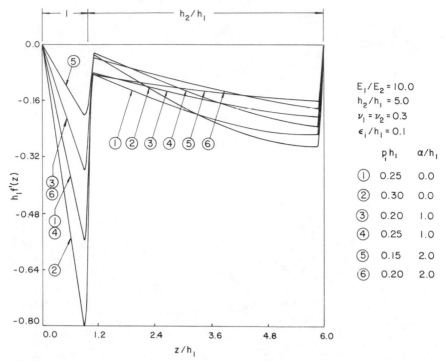

FIG. 12—*The function* $f'(z)$ *which describes the transverse variation of the near-tip, anti-plane shearing stress components.*

is given by $k(z) = KP\sqrt{a}\, f''(z)$. Thus, the z-dependence of the near-tip stress field is controlled by the function $f''(z)$. Some freedom exists in the description of $f''(z)$ through the parameters p_1, α, ε_1, ε_2, and ε_0 as discussed earlier. Various values of these parameters have been considered in an attempt to model the z-dependence of the near-tip solution. Curves showing the resulting functions $f(z)$ are included in Figs. 4 thru 18 and the corresponding calculated values for K are given in Tables 1 thru 4. From these figures, one can see the strong influence of p_1 and α on the character of this solution.

It may be possible to use the tools of classical fracture mechanics for homogeneous materials in conjunction with the model described here for cracked laminates to predict the conditions under which the crack will start to propagate within an individual layer of the composite. As a first approximation, such a local failure would be predicted to occur when the loading reaches a level such that

$$KP\sqrt{a}\, [f''(z)]_{\text{average over the layer}}$$

is equal to the fracture toughness (k_{1c}) for the material constituting that

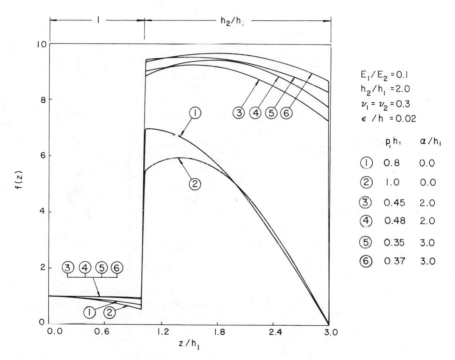

FIG. 13—*The function* f(z) *which governs the transverse variation of the near-tip, normal-stress component.*

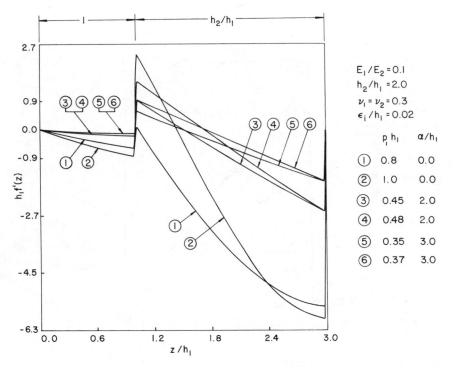

FIG. 14—*The function* f'(z) *which describes the transverse variation of the near-tip, anti-plane shearing stress components.*

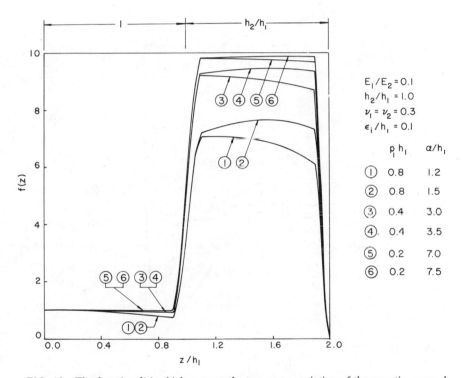

FIG. 15—*The function* f(z) *which governs the transverse variation of the near-tip, normal-stress component.*

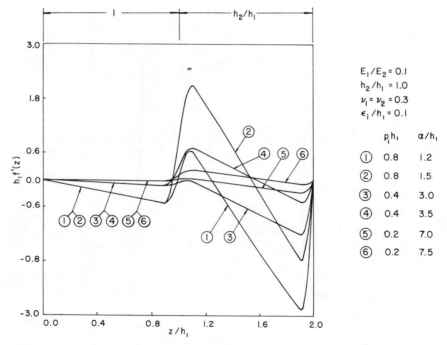

FIG. 16—*The function* f'(z) *which describes the transverse variation of the near-tip, anti-plane shearing stress components.*

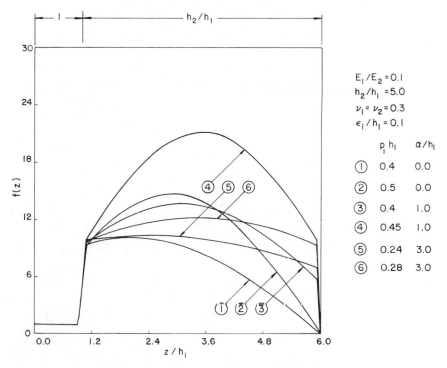

FIG. 17—*The function* f(z) *which governs the transverse variation of the near-tip, normal-stress component.*

layer. This suggests that it is very likely that crack propagation will originate in one of the layers of the composite rather than occurring simultaneously through the thickness. Once some crack growth develops in the "weak" layer, the load will tend to be transferred from that layer to the adjacent ones through the material interface. This procedure is expected to cause either (1) subsequent crack growth in the other layers or (2) delamination depending on the relative strength of the load and the toughness of the layers.

Prediction of the final failure mechanism requires further theoretical and experimental work concerning the detail of properties of interfacial regions. Thus, primary attention has been focused on the asymptotic behavior of the in-plane stress components at the crack tip. Note that the transverse normal stress σ_z is also singular and thus likely to be closely related to prediction of delamination failures. Yet, some comments concerning the character of the transverse shearing stresses in the vicinities of the material interface and the free surfaces are appropriate because they have received a great deal of attention in the published literature. The present model is somewhat ambiguous with respect to the stress com-

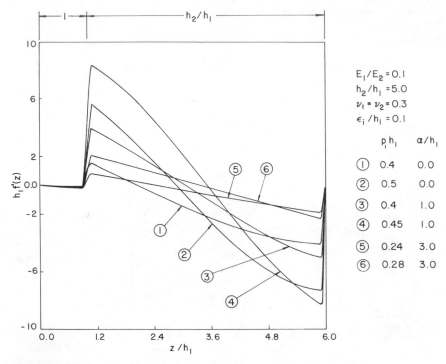

FIG. 18—*The function* f'(z) *which describes the transverse variation of the near-tip, anti-plane shearing stress components.*

ponents in these regions. Recall, the transverse shearing stress components are given by

$$[\tau_{xz}, \tau_{yz}] = f'(z)[Z_x(x, y), Z_y(x, y)]$$

In the transition layer, used to connect the interior solutions from one layer to the next and in the free-surface layer, $f'(z)$ was represented by polynomial expressions which were distinct from the representation of $f(z)$ in the same regions. The reasons for this choice were discussed earlier. Basically, the purpose was to minimize the influence of the uncertainties in these layers on the general character of the solution. It should, however, be pointed out that this representation for $f'(z)$(Eqs 15 and 17) is not expected to accurately model the z-dependence of the shearing stress components in these boundary layers. Indeed, it is likely that their behavior would be reasonably described by the derivative of the function $f(z)$ in this region. If this is the case, the transverse shearing stress components should be significantly larger in the vicinity of the material interfaces and free surfaces than in the interior of the layer.

References

[1] Sih, G. C., Hilton, P. D., Badaliance, R., Shenberger, P. S., and Villarreal, G., "Fracture Mechanics Studies of Composite Systems," Air Force Report AFML-TR-70-112, Part II, June 1971.
[2] Hartranft, R. J. and Sih, G. C., *Journal of Mathematics and Mechanics,* Vol. 19, 1969, pp. 123–138.
[3] Hartranft, R. J. and Sih, G. C., *International Journal of Engineering Science,* Vol. 8, 1970, pp. 711–729.
[4] Badaliance, R. and Sih, G., *Journal of Engineering Fracture Mechanics,* Vol. 7, 1975, pp. 1–22.
[5] Mullinix, B. R. and Smith, C. W., "Distribution of Local Stresses Across the Thickness of Cracked Plates under Bending Fields," *International Journal of Fracture,* to be published.
[6] Villarreal, G., Sih, G. C., and Hartranft, R. J., *Journal of Applied Mechanics,* Vol. 42, 1975, pp. 9–14.

S. S. Wang,[1] *J. F. Mandell,*[1] *F. J. McGarry*[1]

Three-Dimensional Solution for a Through-Thickness Crack in a Cross-Plied Laminate

REFERENCE: Wang, S. S., Mandell, J. F., and McGarry, F. J., "**Three-Dimensional Solution for a Through-Thickness Crack in a Cross-Plied Laminate,**" *Fracture Mechanics of Composites, ASTM STP 593,* American Society for Testing and Materials, 1975, pp. 36–60.

ABSTRACT: A three-dimensional solution is given to the problem of a through-thickness edge crack in a thin 90/0/0/90 laminate under uniform tension normal to the crack direction. The solution is obtained from a three-dimensional finite-element analysis based on the hybrid stress model, and formulated through the Hellinger-Reissner variational principle. The results indicate that the classical $1/\sqrt{r}$ stress singularity is maintained for the in-plane stresses which vary through the thickness and are discontinuous at the ply interface. The interlaminar shear and normal stresses also increase rapidly as the crack tip is approached; the interlaminar shear stresses are always maximum at the ply interface, while the interlaminar normal stress may be maximum at the interface or at the laminate center. The in-plane stresses follow a similar distribution and give an average through-thickness stress-intensity factor similar to two-dimensional predictions. The interlaminar stresses show a strong interaction of the crack tip singular and free-edge effects, as well as a strong influence of the degree of biaxiality of the in-plane stresses. The results suggest several aspects of subsequent subcritical crack extension.

KEY WORDS: fracture properties, composite materials, stress concentration, finite elements, stresses, crack propagation

The problem of a plate containing a through-thickness crack under opening mode loading has been the subject of numerous past investigations for both isotropic and anisotropic materials. For the case of a crack oriented normal to the direction of a uniform, uniaxial applied nominal

---

[1] Research associates and professor, respectively, Department of Materials Science and Engineering, Massachusetts Institute of Technology, Cambridge, Mass. 02139.

stress, σ_∞, the stresses in the plane of the plate near to the crack tip generally take the two-dimensional form [1–5][2]

$$\sigma_{ij} = \frac{K_1}{\sqrt{2\,\pi\,r}}\, f_{ij}\,(\theta,\, s_1,\, s_2) \tag{1}$$

where r and θ are polar coordinates having their origin at the crack tip, and s_1 and s_2 are the complex elastic moduli. K_1, the opening mode stress intensity factor, is a function of the applied stress, specimen geometry, and elastic moduli, and has the form

$$K_1 = \sigma_\infty Y \sqrt{C} \tag{2}$$

where $Y = Y(c/W,\, s_1,\, s_2,\, \alpha)$ in which c is the crack length, W is the specimen width, and α is a geometric factor.

Approximate three-dimensional solutions to the cracked laminate problem suggest that the $\sqrt{r}$ stress singularity will be maintained for the in-plane stresses and that the transverse normal stress in the ith ply will be given by

$$\sigma_{zz} = \nu^{(i)}\,(\sigma_{xx}^{(i)} + \sigma_{yy}^{(i)}) \tag{3}$$

in domains away from free surfaces and ply interfaces, where the plane-strain constraint holds [6]. A further result of three-dimensional considerations is that the stress intensity factor is expected to vary with distance through the thickness of the plate, and to be discontinuous at ply interfaces if the plies have different elastic constants.

The most significant three-dimensional complications arise around the crack tip in the interface region between plies with different elastic constants. Even in the case of an uncracked strip of material, high gradients of interlaminar shear and normal stresses are known to exist near the free edges [7–9]. Experimental observations [10,11] suggest that interlaminar crack extension at the tip of sharp notches plays an important role in the fracture process.

The specific problem for which a solution is presented in this paper is that of a sharp edge crack oriented normal to a uniform applied stress in a thin laminate. The laminate is constructed of four plies oriented at 90/0/0/90 deg to the applied stress direction; each ply is considered to be homogeneous and anisotropic with elastic constants typical of medium modulus graphite/epoxy. A subsequent paper will describe the effects of the extension of a zone of damage at the crack tip.

[2] The italic numbers in brackets refer to the list of references appended to this paper.

Method of Analysis

The method of analysis employed in this study is a three-dimensional finite element analysis based on the hybrid stress model, and formulated through the Hellinger-Reissner variational principle. The use of the hybrid stress model [12–15] enables an accurate description of the high gradient stress fields near the crack tip with a practical number of elements. It also has the important features of allowing for the exact modeling of crack surfaces, free edges, and ply interfaces by suitable adjustments of the appropriately selected stress functions within each element and by the use of Lagrangian multipliers. In the present case, the assumed stress functions were in the form of second-order polynomial expansions, although more efficient choices such as singular functions may be employed if the general character of the stress distribution is previously known [15]. The Hellinger-Reissner variational principle [16, 17] was chosen because it carries out reduced volume integration rather than massive surface integration of the three-dimensional elements, and gives greater accuracy and efficiency.

The analysis employs an eight-node isoparametric hexahedron element which is used in the form of a brick-shaped element for the solution described here. Nine separate sets of stress function are employed for various elements depending upon their particular geometric and boundary conditions; the Lagrangian multiplier technique is also employed in some instances. Details of the development of the analysis, and solutions obtained for several appropriate test cases are given in Ref *18*, and will not be repeated here.

Problem Description

Problem Statement and Basic Assumptions

The first crack problem modeled with the analysis is a through-thickness, single-edge crack as indicated in Fig. 1. The only ply configuration investigated is a balanced (90/0/0/90) laminate with elastic. constants typical of medium-modulus graphite/epoxy. This particular ply configuration has been investigated in detail experimentally, and is also used in a following paper for subcritical crack growth modeling. The crack is oriented in the 90° direction, normal to the applied stress, and is sufficiently long ($c/h_0 = 60$) so that no interaction is expected between the specimen edges and the crack tip effects.

Other studies [15, 19] have demonstrated that an optimum aspect ratio of finite element dimensions is to be expected for the three-dimensional, hybrid stress finite element. Since the problem to be solved is that of a thin plate, a two-stage solution technique is employed both to

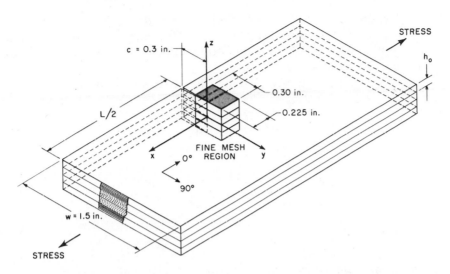

FIG. 1—*Through-thickness crack in a 90/0/0/90 laminate showing geometry, coordinate system, and FEM fine mesh region.*

keep the final element dimensions in a reasonable ratio and to test the convergence of the solution. The two-stage solution is obtained as follows: a solution which models the entire specimen as reduced by symmetry conditions is first obtained, and then the displacement field from this solution is used as the boundary conditions for an inner solution which only covers the region near the crack tip. Figure 1 shows the size of the inner region, which is chosen so that the elements near the crack tip have approximately equal dimensions on all sides. Displacement boundary conditions are imposed in the inner region analysis because these are expected to give a better solution, and to save computation time in the initial solution.

Several basic assumptions are inherent to this analysis:

1. The laminate is initially flat.
2. Each ply is a continuum with anisotropic elastic constants; individual fibers and matrix are not considered.
3. Unless delamination regions are specifically modeled, the plies are assumed to be perfectly bonded together. No adhesive layer is included in this study.
4. The stress-strain relations for all elastic constants are assumed to be linear.

Geometry and Elastic Constants

The through-thickness crack specimen shown in Fig. 1 has a length, L, of two times the width, W, a ply thickness of $h_0 = W/300$, and a crack length of $c = W/5$. In relating these dimensions to laminates studied elsewhere [18] experimentally, $h_o = 0.005$ in., so that $W = 1.5$ in., $L = 3.0$ in., and $c = 0.30$ in. A uniformly distributed stress, σ_∞, is applied at the boundaries $x = \pm L/2$.

The ply elastic constants used in this study are typical of medium modulus graphite/epoxy:

$$E_{LL} = 18.25 \times 10^6 \text{ psi}$$

$$E_{TT} = E_{zz} = 1.50 \times 10^6 \text{ psi}$$

$$G_{LT} = G_{Lz} = G_{Tz} = 0.95 \times 10^6 \text{ psi}$$

$$\nu_{LT} = \nu_{Lz} = \nu_{Tz} = 0.24$$

Symmetry and Boundary Conditions

The balanced, symmetric ply configuration allows modeling of only the upper two plies, so that the boundary displacement conditions are

$$u(x, y, z) = u(x, y, -z)$$
$$v(x, y, z) = v(x, y, -z) \qquad (4)$$
$$w(x, y, z) = -w(x, y, -z)$$

The last equation of displacement symmetry also implies

$$w(x, y, 0) = 0$$

that is, over the mid-plane of the laminate, the normal displacement, w, vanishes everywhere.

Further simplification can be made due to the (90/0/0/90) ply configuration of the laminate used. The in-plane displacement, u, at the symmetry plane $x = 0$ ahead of the crack tip yields.

$$u(0, y, z) = 0 \qquad (5)$$

However, it should be noted that this symmetry condition is not applicable for the single-edge-notched plate of an angle ply laminate [20].

The appropriate stress boundary conditions for the problem considered here are traction-free boundary conditions from three-dimensional elasticity. For example, the traction-free boundary conditions along the crack flanks are

$$\sigma_{xx}(0, y, z) = 0$$
$$\sigma_{xy}(0, y, z) = 0 \qquad -c \leqslant y \leqslant 0 \qquad (6)$$
$$\sigma_{xz}(0, y, z) = 0$$

The applied tractions along the ends of the laminate are

$$\sigma_{xx}(\pm L/2, y, z) = \sigma_{\infty}$$
$$\sigma_{xy}(\pm L/2, y, z) = 0 \qquad (7)$$
$$\sigma_{xz}(\pm L/2, y, z) = 0$$

Also, on the mid-plane of the laminate, $z = 0$

$$\sigma_{xz}(x, y, 0) = 0$$
$$\sigma_{yz}(x, y, 0) = 0 \qquad (8)$$
$$\text{but } \sigma_{zz}(x, y, 0) \neq 0$$

It should be noted that these mid-plane shear-free conditions, Eq 8, the crack flank traction-free conditions, Eq 6, as well as the normal surface-free conditions

$$\sigma_{xz}(x, y, 2h_0) = 0$$
$$\sigma_{yz}(x, y, 2h_0) = 0$$
$$\sigma_{zz}(x, y, 2h_0) = 0$$

and

$$\sigma_{yy}(x, -c, z) = \sigma_{yy}(x, d, z) = 0$$
$$\sigma_{yx}(x, -c, z) = \sigma_{yx}(x, d, z) = 0$$
$$\sigma_{yz}(x, -c, z) = \sigma_{yz}(x, d, z) = 0$$

where $d = W - c$, are inherently satisfied during the formulation of the stiffness matrix.

Employing the symmetry and boundary conditions and the following geometric symmetry conditions for the (90/0/0/90) case

$$\sigma_{xy}(0, y, z) = 0$$
$$0 \leqslant y \leqslant d$$
$$\sigma_{xz}(0, y, z) = 0$$

The region under study has thus been reduced to one quadrant of the whole plate.

Finite Element Discretization

The upper quadrant of the laminate was modeled with a relatively coarse finite element mesh of $9 \times 18 \times 2$ elements in the x, y, and z directions, respectively, for a total of 570 nodes. The inner mesh was then constructed over the region shown in Fig. 1, using the displacements from the upper quadrant (coarse mesh) as boundary conditions. The inner mesh contains $11 \times 19 \times 4$ elements as shown in Fig. 2; the dimensions of the smallest elements are approximately equal to the ply thickness. (Since only the

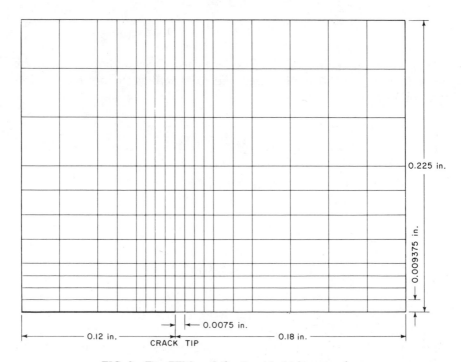

FIG. 2—*Fine FEM mesh for through-thickness crack.*

negative x-direction is considered, the sign of x is dropped in the remainder of the paper.)

Numerical Results

The results of the inner mesh solution are described in detail in this section. There is obvious difficulty in describing the three-dimensional stress field about a crack tip, and emphasis has been placed on those stresses and directions which are thought to be most interesting.

Figures 3 and 4 give the in-plane stresses ahead of the crack tip for the coarse and fine mesh solutions. The results from both solutions are in good agreement except near to the crack tip, where the fine mesh is necessary to achieve accurate results. Figures 5 and 6 give log-log plots of all of the in-plane stresses ahead of and normal to the crack as a function of distance from the crack tip. The data for each case are compared to the classical $\sqrt{r}$ stress singularity, and good agreement is found in all cases. Thus, the in-plane stresses near the crack tip conform to the classical stress singularity. The in-plane stresses are discontinuous from ply to ply due to the difference in modulus of each ply, and vary only slightly through the thickness of each ply.

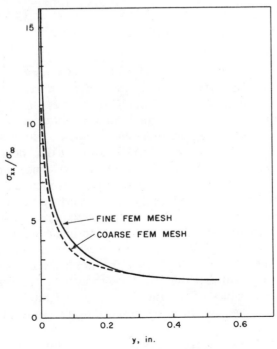

FIG. 3—σ_{xx} at the mid-plane of 0° ply along x = 0.

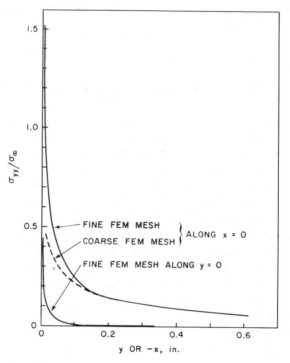

FIG. 4—σ_{yy} at the mid-plane of 0° ply along x = 0 and y = 0.

The interlaminar shear stresses have been plotted along several directions as functions of distance from the crack tip and as functions of the z-coordinate at several individual points. Figure 7 gives the interlaminar shear-stress distribution ahead of the crack tip at the interface and at $z = 3h_0/4$; the stresses build up rapidly after changing sign within a distance from the crack tip approximately equal to the laminate thickness. Figure 8 gives the interlaminar shear stresses as functions of distance through the thickness at several points ahead of the crack tip. σ_{xz} is identically zero on the $y - z$ plane, but σ_{yz} builds up rapidly as the interface between plies is approached. Figure 9a,b and 10a,b give the interlaminar shear stresses along the x-axis, normal to the crack direction. In this case, as well as at an intermediate direction in Figure 11, the same general characteristics are observed as along the y-axis. In most cases, the interlaminar shear stresses go through a sign reversal and then increase sharply as the crack tip is approached, reaching values of the same order of magnitude as the applied stress. The interlaminar shear stresses are always maximum at the interface.

The interlaminar normal stress, σ_{zz}, is of particular importance in 0/90 laminates. Figures 12, 13, and 14 give the distribution of σ_{zz} as a function

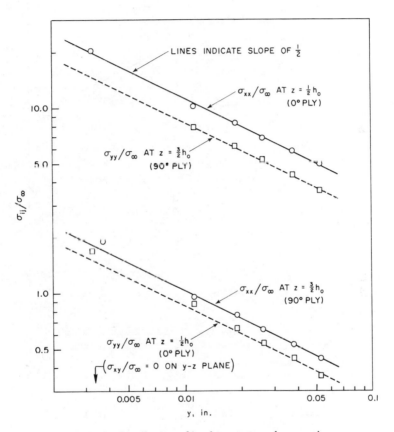

FIG. 5—*Distribution of in-plane stresses along y-axis.*

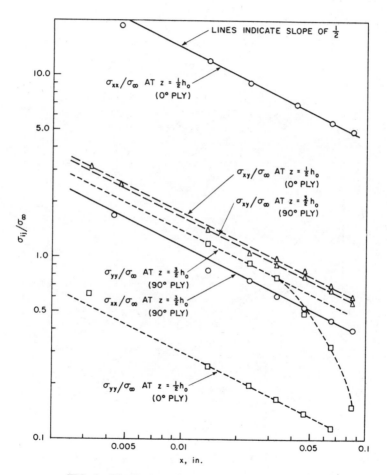

FIG. 6—*Distribution of in-plane stresses along x-axis.*

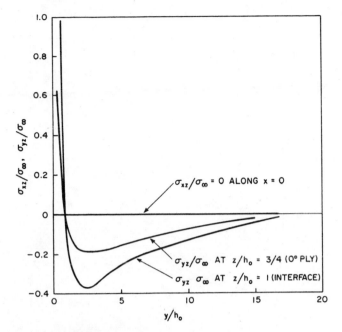

FIG. 7—*Distribution of σ_{xz} and σ_{yz} at $z/h_0 = 0.75$ and 1.0 along y-axis.*

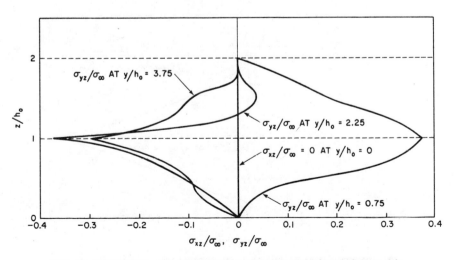

FIG. 8—*Distribution of σ_{xz} and σ_{yz} through laminate thickness along y-axis.*

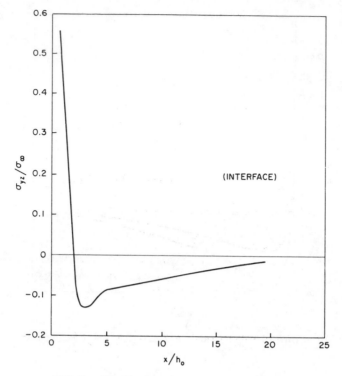

FIG. 9a—Distribution of σ_{yz} at $z = h_0$ along x-axis.

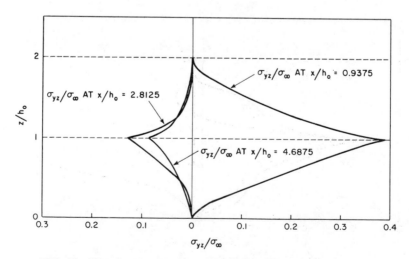

FIG. 9b—Distribution of σ_{yz} through laminate thickness along x-axis.

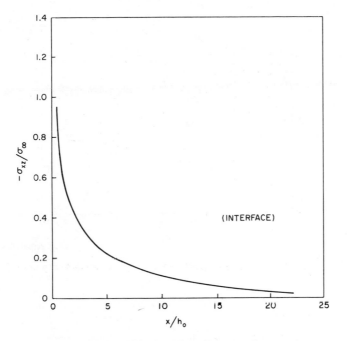

FIG. 10a—Distribution of σ_{xz} at $z = h_0$ along x axis.

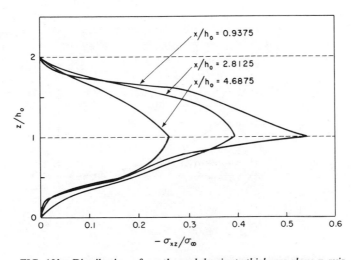

FIG. 10b—Distribution of σ_{xz} through laminate thickness along x-axis.

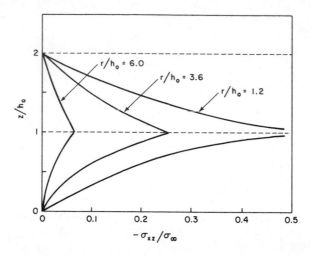

FIG. 11—*Distribution of σ_{xz} through laminate thickness along $\theta = 51.34°$.*

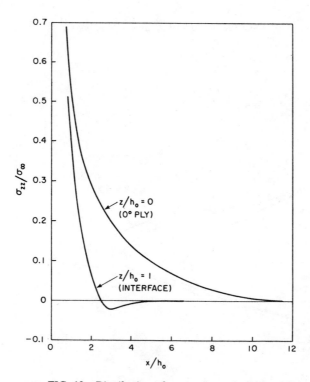

FIG. 12—*Distribution of σ_{zz} at $z/h_0 = 1$ along x-axis.*

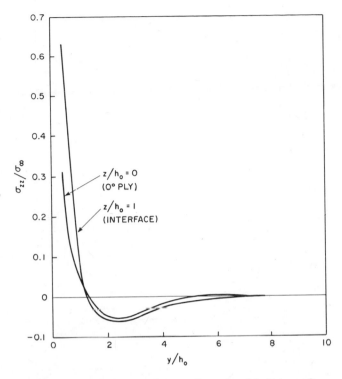

FIG. 13—*Distribution of σ_{zz} at a/h$_0$ = 0 and 1 along y-axis.*

of distance from the crack tip along the x and y-axes and at 45°. The value of σ_{zz} reaches levels similar to the interlaminar shear stresses over a region of similar dimension. In most cases a change in sign of σ_{zz} is observed at some distance from the crack tip.

The rapidly rising interlaminar stresses near the crack tip suggest an interlaminar stress singularity. The log-log plot of σ_{zz} in Figure 15 appears to follow a $\sqrt{r}$ singularity in the region very near to the crack tip; however, the accuracy of the analysis within this domain may be subject to question, and a still finer finite-element mesh solution may be required to firmly establish the existence of singular behavior.

The through-thickness profiles of σ_{zz} along the x and y-axes and an intermediate direction are given in Figs. 16, 17, and 18. The distributions along the x-axis and the intermediate direction are similar, with the maximum stress at the mid-plane of the laminate in most cases, particularly near the crack tip; further out from the crack tip the distribution is irregular along the intermediate direction, indicating a transitional behavior. Along the y-axis the stress is maximum at the interface in most cases.

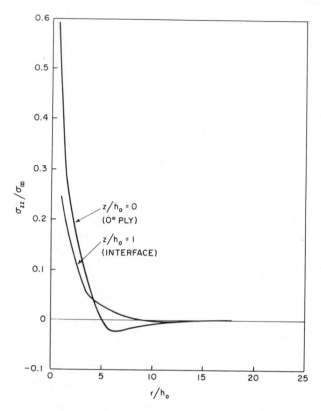

FIG. 14—*Distribution of σ_{zz} at $z/h_0 = 0$ and 1 along $\theta = 45°$.*

Discussion

In-Plane Stress Distributions

Figures 5 and 6 indicate that the in-plane stresses follow the classical $\sqrt{r}$ stress singularity over a region extending for at least a distance of $c/10$ away from the crack tip, and much further in many cases. The in-plane stresses vary only slightly with the z-coordinate within a ply, but are discontinuous across the 0/90-ply interface, reflecting the difference in modulus of each ply for a particular direction.

It is of interest to compare the in-plane stress distributions obtained from the three-dimensional solution with the distribution predicted by two-dimensional theory. The two-dimensional stress distribution was obtained by the following procedure: (1) the laminate moduli were determined following the procedure in Ref. *21* from the ply moduli given previously;

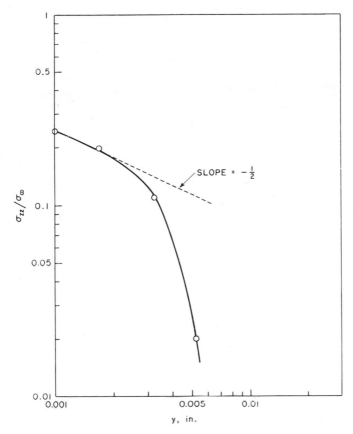

FIG. 15—*Strength of singularity of σ_{zz} along y-axis.*

(2) the stress intensity factor, K_I, was determined from a two-dimensional finite element K-calibration [5]; and (3) the stress distribution was determined from Eq 1 using appropriate values of s_1 and s_2 [4]. Figure 19 indicates that while the magnitudes of the stresses are different, the shapes of isostress contours of σ_{xx} are nearly the same for the two and three-dimensional solutions (the contours are plotted by a computer routine and give only the approximate locations of the isostress contours, with particularly significant inaccuracies near to the crack tip). This result is in contrast to the results for a $\pm 45°$ laminate given in Ref *20* where the shape of the distributions obtained from a similar analysis were different in each ply and were strongly different from the two-dimensional case. These results suggest that the two and three-dimensional solutions will produce different isostress contour shapes unless the material axes for each ply are aligned with the structural axes of the problem.

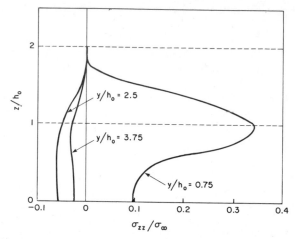

FIG. 16—*Distribution of σ_{zz} through laminate thickness along y-axis.*

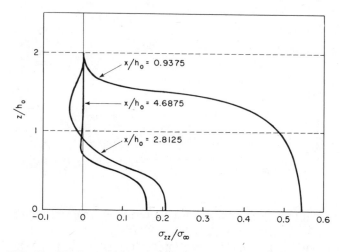

FIG. 17—*Distribution of σ_{zz} through laminate thickness along x-axis.*

The intensity of the stresses obtained from the two and three-dimensional solutions is also of interest. A comparison of the two solutions can be made by averaging the stress through the thickness at a given point for the three-dimensional solution, and then comparing with the two-dimensional value. For example, the average value of $\sigma_{xx}/\sigma_{\infty}$ at a distance of 0.01875 in. directly ahead of the crack tip is 4.52, which yields an average stress intensity factor of $K_1 = 1.55$ for a unit applied stress. This is approximately 20 percent higher than the two-dimensional K_1 value of 1.33.

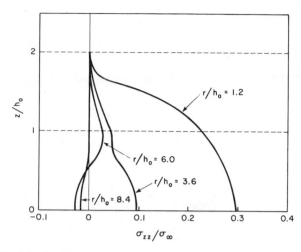

FIG. 18—*Distribution of* $\sigma_{zz}/\sigma_\infty$ *through laminate thickness along* $\theta = 51.34°$.

The foregoing comparisons indicate that the three-dimensional solution gives approximately the same magnitude and distribution of the average in-plane stresses as does classical two-dimensional theory. It is possible that a greater discrepancy would be found for regions very close to the crack tip, where the interlaminar stresses are more significant, but the present solution may not be accurate inside a region approximately one ply thickness away from the crack tip. Determination of the reasons for the relatively small differences in K_I values obtained from two and three-dimensional solutions will also require further study of the various parameters involved. It should be emphasized that comparisons of the three-dimensional results with two-dimensional theory tend to obscure the truly three-dimensional nature of the stress field; for example, the stress intensity factor is not a constant, but is a function of the z-coordinate even for the in-plane stresses.

Interlaminar Stress Distributions

The interlaminar stress results are restricted by the size of the finite-element mesh used in the solution. While the interlaminar stresses clearly increase rapidly as the crack tip is approached, a definitive study of such aspects as the possible singular behavior of the stresses will require further solutions with finer mesh sizes. However, several interesting aspects of the interlaminar stress distributions are evident in the results now available.

One important characteristic of the interlaminar stress distribution curves is their general shape and sign. Many of the curves show a sign reversal, as in Figs. 7 and 13, while others show a monotonically

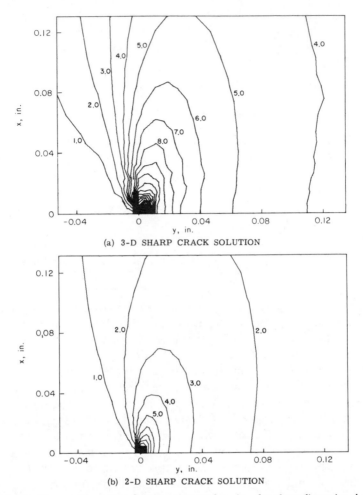

FIG. 19—*Comparison of isostress contours of* $\sigma_{xx}/\sigma_\infty$ *for three-dimensional solution at mid-plane of 0° ply and two-dimensional solution.*

increasing stress, such as Fig. 10*a*. The sign reversal is particularly interesting in the case of σ_{zz} as the plane-strain effect given by Eq 3 predicts a monotonically increasing tensile stress, while Fig. 13 indicates a sign reversal with the stress becoming tensile as the crack tip is approached. Even very close to the crack tip, as in Fig. 15, the value of σ_{zz} is approximately an order of magnitude lower than that predicted by Eq 3, and the maximum value occurs at the ply interface rather than at the laminate center. The origin of the sign reversal may be related to the free edge effect associated with the crack flanks as the sign of σ_{zz} is negative near a free edge for the 90/0/0/90 laminate in an unnotched strip [9, 18]. The ratio of σ_{zz} to the in-plane stresses near the free edge of the unnotched strip is also similar in magnitude to that near the crack tip in the present solution. Thus, an interaction between the free edge/ply interface effects and the crack tip singularity effects may have a strong influence on the interlaminar stress distributions.

Another probable influence is the degree of biaxiality of the in-plane stresses. Figures 5 and 6 indicate that σ_{xx} in the 0° ply is much greater than all other stresses along the x-axis; while σ_{xx} in the 0° ply and σ_{yy} in the 90° ply are nearly equal along the y-axis. Figures 16, 17, and 18 indicate a transition in the position of the maximum value of σ_{zz} from the interface to the center of the laminate along the various directions. This effect may be regarded as one example of a possible coupling between the in-plane and interlaminar stresses, and it may have an influence on the interlaminar stress distributions in addition to that of the free edge/ply interface effect.

It is also of interest to note the general shape of the interlaminar shear-stress curves as functions of the z-coordinate. Figures 9b, 10b, and 11 indicate that the interlaminar shear stresses are not restricted to regions near the ply interface. The value of the interlaminar shear stresses is always a maximum at the interface but is also high at the center of the ply, so the entire ply thickness is affected by the interlaminar stresses.

Implications for Local Crack Extension

Prediction of crack extension requires not only as analytical determination of local crack-tip stress distribution, but also the application of an appropriate criterion for the initiation and propagation of subcracks from the main crack tip. However, the present solution suggests several instances where damage may be expected to occur as the result of one dominant stress component.

Initial damage at a crack tip is shown in Refs 18 and 20 to take the form of a through-ply thickness subcrack propagating radially along the fibers of each ply. Figure 6 indicates that the stress σ_{xy} is nearly an order of magnitude greater than any other stress tending to form the subcrack in the 0° ply along the x-axis, while Fig. 5 indicates that σ_{xx} is the greatest stress tending to form the subcrack in the 90° ply along the y-axis. Thus, the 0° subcrack is apparently shear-induced, while the 90° split is apparently tension-induced since the strength in each case is similar in magnitude. After the subcracks are formed these observations may no longer be valid for the growing subcrack, as is discussed in a subsequent paper.

The interlaminar stresses are distributed over a very local region at the crack tip, with significant stress levels extending outward from the crack tip for a distance of several ply thicknesses. A simple criterion for the extension of an interlaminar failure zone according to a condition of the interlaminar strength level would predict a failure zone on the order of one or two-ply thicknesses. Reference *18* indicates that this is the approximate dimension of the interlaminar failure zone measured experimentally for a graphite/epoxy laminate of the 90/0/0/90-ply configuration. The application of such a criterion is meaningful only in the absence of other damage such as 0° and 90° subcracks; since such subcracks usually are observed to precede or accompany delamination, their influence on the distribution of the interlaminar stresses must be considered.

Limitations of the Results

As in any numerical solution, the accuracy of the results is limited by the fineness of the element discretization. The in-plane stress distributions are thought to be determined accurately over the domain where data are plotted, as in Figs. 5 and 6. The in-plane stresses vary only slightly through the thickness of each ply, and so the singular behavior demonstrated in the figures is also observed for other values of z. The behavior closer to the crack tip than the points shown is necessarily uncertain, and would require a solution using a finer finite element mesh. Similarly, the interlaminar stresses cannot be determined arbitrarily close to the crack tip, and a meaningful test of their singularity is not possible without a finer mesh solution.

Conclusions

The full three-dimensional stress distribution is given for a sharp edge crack in a 90/0/0/90 graphite/epoxy laminate, with the exception of those regions which were too localized to the crack tip for accurate analysis with the finite element meshes employed. The results indicate that the in-plane stresses follow the classical $1/\sqrt{r}$ stress singularity in that portion of the near-crack tip region which was studied; the interlaminar stresses also increase rapidly as the crack tip is approached, in many cases following a sign reversal further away from the crack tip. Contrary to earlier results for angle-plied laminates, the inplane stresses for the 90/0/0/90 laminate follow similar isostress contour shapes as predicted by two-dimensional theory, although their numerical values are different. The magnitude of the in-plane stresses varies through the thickness and is discontinuous at the ply interfaces, but the average value gives a stress intensity factor which is similar to the two-dimensional prediction. The interlaminar stresses show a strong interaction between the crack-tip stress field and the free-edge effects, and also a strong coupling of in-plane and interlaminar stresses due to the degree of biaxiality of the in-plane stresses.

The results suggest several possibilities for subsequent subcritical crack extension.

Acknowledgment

This work was sponsored by the Air Force Materials Laboratory through Contract F33615-73-C-5169. The authors gratefully acknowledge this support.

References

[1] Williams, M. L., *Journal of Applied Mechanics,* Transactions, American Society of Mechanical Engineers, Vol. 24, 1957, p. 109.

[2] Irwin, G. R., Kies, J. A., and Smith, H. L. in *Proceedings,* American Society for Testing and Materials, Vol. 58, 1958, p. 640.

[3] Wu, E. M., "Application of Fracture Mechanics to Orthotropic Plates," T & M Report No. 248, University of Illinois, 1963.

[4] Sih, G. C. and Liebowitz, H. in *Fracture: An Advanced Treatise,* H. Liebowitz, Ed., Vol. 2, Academic Press, New York, 1968, p. 67.

[5] Mandell, J. F., McGarry, F. J., Wang, S. S., and Im, J., *Journal of Composite Materials,* Vol. 8, 1974, p. 106.

[6] Hilton, P. D., Sih, G. C., and Badaliance, R., "Analytical Modelling of Laminate Composites with Application to Through-Crack Problems," Technical Report AFML-TR-70-112, Part IV, Wright-Patterson AFB, Dec. 1973.

[7] Puppo, A. H. and Evensen, H. A., *Journal of Composite Materials,* Vol. 4, 1970, p. 538.

[8] Pipes, R. B. and Pagano, N. J., *Journal of Composite Materials,* Vol. 4, 1970, p. 538.

[9] Pipes, R. B., "Solutions of Certain Problems in the Theory of Elasticity for Laminated Anisotropic Systems," Ph.D. thesis, University of Texas, Arlington, Tex., March 1972.

[10] Mandell, J. F., McGarry, F. J., Kashihara, R., and Bishop, W. O., "Engineering Aspects of Fracture Toughness: Fiber Reinforced Laminates," *Proceedings,* 29th Reinforced Plastics Composites Div., Society of the Plastics Industry, 1974, Section 17D.

[11] Mandell, J. F., McGarry, F. J., Im, J., and Meier, U., "Fiber Orientation, Crack Velocity, and Cyclic Loading Effects on the Mode of Crack Extension in Fiber Reinforced Plastics," presented at TMS/AIME Failure Modes in Composites II Conference, 1974.

[12] Pian, T. H. H., *AIAA Journal,* Vol. 2, 1964, p. 1333.

[13] Pian, T. H. H. and Tong, P., "Basis of Finite Element Methods for Solid Continua," *International Journal for Numerical Methods in Engineering,* Vol. 1, 1969.

[14] Pian, T. H. H., Tong, P., and Luk, C. H., "Elastic Crack Analysis by a Finite Element Hybrid Method," paper presented at the Third Conference on Matrix Methods in Structural Mechanics, Wright-Patterson Air Force Base, Ohio, 1972.

[15] Luk, C. H., "Assumed Stress Hybrid Finite Element Method for Fracture Mechanics and Elastic-Plastic Analysis," PhD. thesis, Aero and Astro Dept., Massachusetts Institute of Technology, 1972.

[16] Reissner, E., "On Variational Principles in Elasticity," Symposium Calculus of Variations and Applications, American Mathematical Society, April 1956.

[17] Hellinger E., Die Allegemeinen Ansatze der Mechanik der Kontinua. Art. 30, in F. Klein and C. Muller, Eds., *Encyklopadie Mathematischen Weissenchaften,* mit Einschluss Ihrer Anwendunge, Vol IV/4, Mechanik, 601-94, Teuber: Leipzig, 1954.

[*18*] Mandell, J. F., Wang, S. S., and McGarry, F. J., "Fracture of Graphite Fiber Reinforced Composites," Technical Report AFML-TR-74-167, Wright-Patterson AFB, Ohio, 1974.

[*19*] Lee, S. W., "An Assumed Stress Hybrid Finite Element for Three Dimensional Elastic Structural Analysis," S. M. thesis, Aero & Astro Dept., Massachusetts Institute of Technology, 1974.

[*20*] Mandell, J. F., Wang, S. S., and McGarry, F. J., "Fracture of Graphite Fiber Reinforced Composites," Technical Report AFML-TR-73-142, Wright-Patterson AFB, Ohio, 1973.

[*21*] Chamis, C. C., "Micro and Structural Mechanics and Structural Synthesis of Multi-layered Filament Composite Panels," Report No. 9, Div. of Solid Mechanics and Mechanical Design, Case Western Reserve University, 1968.

S. S. Wang,[1] *J. F. Mandell,*[1] *and F. J. McGarry*[1]

Three-Dimensional Solution for a Through-Thickness Crack with Crack Tip Damage in a Cross-Plied Laminate

REFERENCE: Wang, S. S., Mandell, J. F., and McGarry, F. J., **"Three-Dimensional Solution for a Through-Thickness Crack with Crack Tip Damage in a Cross-Plied Laminate,"***Fracture Mechanics of Composites, ASTM STP 593,* American Society for Testing and Materials, 1975, pp. 61–85.

ABSTRACT: A three-dimensional finite-element solution is given for the stress field of a 0/90 laminate containing a sharp through-thickness edge crack with crack tip damage consisting of subcracks parallel to the fibers of each ply. The solution is compared to that for a sharp crack with no subcracks given in an associated paper, and the introduction of the subcracks is shown to significantly alter the stress field. Outside of a core zone at the main crack tip, the two stress distributions are nearly identical. Inside of the core zone, the subcracks serve to relax the in-plane stresses in a manner similar to the action of a plastic zone in a metal; the mechanisms of stress transfer around the subcracks are identified. The results also indicate that the fundamental fracture mechanics concept of a zone of relaxed stresses near the main crack tip, surrounded by an undisturbed singular stress field, is preserved, and that the subcracks cause no shift in the singular stress field which would require a crack length correction.

KEY WORDS: fracture properties, composite materials, stress concentration, finite elements, stresses, crack propagation

In a related paper, a three-dimensional solution has been given for the problem of a sharp through-thickness edge crack in a 90/0/0/90 laminate. While sharp crack problems are fundamental to the study of crack propagation in brittle materials, it is clear that for any real engineering material, some mechanism of crack blunting must be available to avoid immediate failure from the singular stress field at the crack tip when even the smallest of loads is applied. Practical flaws and other stress-concentrators in real materials, while never perfectly sharp, still necessitate some form of materials "yielding" to avoid failure at very low stress levels.

The initial "yielding" of many types of fiber reinforced plastics has been shown to take the form of subcritical cracks (termed subcracks) ex-

[1] Research associates and professor, respectively, Department of Materials Science and Engineering, Massachusetts Institute of Technology, Cambridge, Mass. 02139.

tending outward from the main crack tip, parallel to the fibers of each ply of material [1–6],[2] with a zone of interlaminar separation extending simultaneously in some cases [4–6]. If a sharp notch is machined into a tensile strip, a zone of such subcracks, and in some cases delaminations, may be observed to extend in a stable manner with increasing applied stress, forming a pattern of small through-ply cracks extending outward from the machined notch tip in a radial array, parallel to the fibers of each ply; the subcracks may extend independently or may be interconnected by zones of inter-ply delamination. At some critical value of applied stress, a catastropic separation will propagate from the machined notch to cause complete failure.

To the author's knowledge, no rigorous analytical solution to the problem of a notch containing subcracks and delaminations has been presented in the literature, apparently because of the inherent singular and three-dimensional nature of the problem, and the complexity of the crack tip geometry in the laminate structure. Approximate two-dimensional macroscopic models have been employed to predict the deflection of a crack in a unidirectional composite from an orientation normal to the fibers to an orientation parallel to the fibers [7–9], and to predict the extension of the deflected crack (in this case modeled as an extended plastic zone) parallel to the fiber direction at the crack tip [10]. Other solutions have been given for various simplified microscale models of interlaminar and interface cracks [11, 12].

The object of the present study has been to provide a rigorous three-dimensional solution on the macroscopic scale for a single example of a notch containing subcracks in a realistic laminate. The particular problem chosen is that of a through-thickness edge crack in a 90/0/0/90 laminate which contains subcracks propagating outward from the main crack tip parallel to the fibers of each 0° and 90° ply. The lengths of the subcritical, through-ply cracks were taken from experimental observations of tests on graphite/epoxy specimens, which have been reported elsewhere [5]. Although a small amount of delamination between plies also was observed at higher loads in these tests, this has not been included in the present solution.

The specimen dimensions, ply arrangement, and ply elastic constants used for the associated sharp-crack solution all have been duplicated in the present case, so that direct comparisons of the resulting stress distributions may be made. The method of analysis also is the same as that employed in the associated solution: a three-dimensional finite-element analysis using the hybrid stress model, and formulated through the Hellinger-Reissner variational principle [5].

---

[2] The italic numbers in brackets refer to the list of references appended to this paper.

Problem Description and Modeling

Geometry of Subcracks

The geometry of the problem is described in Fig. 1. A through-thickness crack identical to the case studied in the associated paper is situated normal to the applied stress. Subcracks extend from the tip of the through-thickness crack; the subcracks penetrate the thickness of a single ply and propagate parallel to the fiber direction of the ply. The subcrack in the top, 90°, ply is of length $c_{90} = 0.09$ in. along the y-axis, and extends through the thickness only from $z = h_0$ to $z = 2h_0$, but does not extend into the 0° ply; an identical c_{90} is assumed to exist in the bottom ply. The subcrack in the center, 0°, plies is of length $c_0 = 0.20$ in. along the positive x-axis. The c_0 subcrack penetrates from $z = -h_0$ to $z = +h_0$, and an identical c_0 crack is assumed to propagate along the x-axis in the negative direction, so that the total length of the subcrack in the 0° ply is $2c_0$. In the analysis it is assumed that the plies remain perfectly bonded together in all regions.

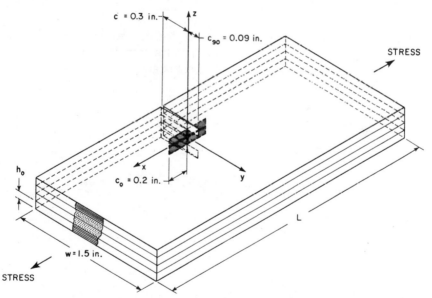

FIG. 1—*Through-thickness crack with subcracks in a 90/0/0/90 laminate showing geometry and coordinate.*

It should be emphasized that the choice of c_0 and c_{90} cannot be arbitrary. The relative length of subcracks in each ply varies with the ply configuration, and no analytical method has yet been employed to predict the length. Since the length is important to the stress distribution, realistic values must be adopted in modeling the problem. The values of c_0 and c_{90} used in the present case come from experimental measurements given in Ref 5 for specimens of identical size and shape, and similar elastic constants, to those used in the analysis. The major differences in the experimental case are that some local delamination between plies was observed at higher stresses, and that the notch tip was not infinitely sharp [5]. The values of c_0 and c_{90} correspond to those measured experimentally at an applied stress of 28.8 ksi, or a macroscopic value of K_1 of approximately 37.4 ksi$\sqrt{}$ in. The subcrack surfaces are assumed to be free of friction.

Symmetry and Boundary Conditions

The same symmetry and boundary conditions are assumed as for the through-thickness sharp crack problem except as noted, plus additional displacement and traction boundary conditions for the c_0 and c_{90} subcracks.

The displacement boundary conditions for the $0°$ layers along the c_{90} subcrack are

$$u(\pm 0, y, z) = 0$$

where $0 \leqslant y \leqslant c_{90}$ and $0 \leqslant z \leqslant h_0$.

The constraints on displacement imposed for the through-thickness crack are released on the c_{90} crack surfaces. The traction-free boundary conditions for the surfaces of the c_{90} subcrack are

$$\sigma_{xx}(\pm 0, y, z) = 0$$
$$\sigma_{xy}(\pm 0, y, z) = 0$$
$$\sigma_{xz}(\pm 0, y, z) = 0$$

for $0 \leqslant y \leqslant c_{90}$ and $h_0 \leqslant z \leqslant 2h_0$. Similarly, for the c_0 subcrack

$$\sigma_{xy}(x, \pm 0, z) = 0$$
$$\sigma_{yy}(x, \pm 0, z) = 0$$
$$\sigma_{yz}(x, \pm 0, z) = 0$$

where $0 \leqslant x \leqslant c_0$ and $0 \leqslant z \leqslant h_0$.

Finite Element Discretization

Figure 2 gives the finite-element mesh for the $0°$ ply. The mesh consists of 315 elements in the plane, with two elements through the half-thickness, one for each ply. The solution in this case was single-stage with a mesh

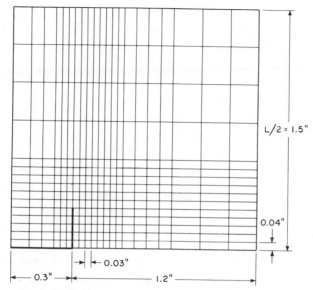

FIG. 2—*Finite-element mesh for 0° ply with subcrack c_0.*

slightly coarser than the fine mesh in the sharp-crack solution. The smallest elements in the present case had in-plane dimensions approximately four times as large as for the inner mesh of the sharp-crack solution.

Numerical Results

In most cases the results are plotted along lines parallel to the principle axes to indicate the behavior of the stress field as the c_0 and c_{90} subcracks are approached and crossed. The more interesting aspects of the stress distribution are concentrated in the regions near the subcracks, particularly where the stress is transferred across the c_0 subcrack as the main (through-thickness) crack attempts to open under the applied stress. Figure 3 indicates the planar displacement field of the 0° ply at an exaggerated scale; the c_0 subcrack is clearly tending to open and shear, while the crack flanks show a high degree of rotation. Thus, we may expect a significant disturbance as the 90° ply, which is continuous over the c_0 subcrack, is sheared and stretched in reaction to the displacement tendencies of the 0° ply. Similar, but less significant effects occur along the c_{90} subcrack as it attempts to open.

In-Plane Stresses

Introduction of subcracks of length similar to the main crack produces the anticipated severe disturbance in most of the stress components. However, the disturbance is surprisingly localized, and the in-plane stresses

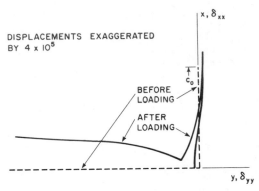

FIG. 3—*Displacement of 0° ply with c_0 subcrack after application of unit applied stress* (z = 0).

rapidly return to approximately the same value as for the through-thickness crack problem without subcracks.

Figures 4 and 5 give the distribution of σ_{xx} in the 0° ply along lines of constant x and y. Figure 5 is particularly interesting as it shows the dramatic effect of c_0 on σ_{xx} along the two sides of the subcrack; the curves at $y = 0^+$ and 0^- would be identical in the absence of the split, but with the split, the 0^+ curve reaches very high stress levels as the 0^- curve goes into compression. A similarly extreme distortion is evident for σ_{xx} in the 90° ply, indicated in Fig. 6.

Figures 7 and 8 give the transverse stress σ_{yy} in the 0° ply. Figure 7 indicates that σ_{yy} reaches a maximum at some value of y out from the c_0 subcrack. Figures 9 and 10 give σ_{yy} in the 90° ply.

Figures 11 thru 15 give the distributions of σ_{xy}. The effect of c_0 and the shearing action along it is particularly evident in Fig. 13, which gives σ_{xy} in the 90° ply along lines of constant x, which cross above the 0° subcrack. Figure 16 compares σ_{xy} along the x-axis in the 0° and 90° plies. The stress in the 90° ply gradually decreases from its maximum at $x = 0$, while in the 0° ply $\sigma_{xy} = 0$ along the subcrack, and is then approximately equal to that in the 90° ply for $x > c_0$.

Interlaminar Stresses

The interlaminar shear stresses are given at the interface in regions near the subcritical cracks in Figures 17 thru 20. The values of σ_{yz} are in most cases much smaller than σ_{xz}. Figure 19 is the most interesting case since it describes σ_{xz} across c_0 at various points; as expected, very high levels of σ_{xz} are reached as the two sides of the subcrack tend to displace relative to each other.

Figures 21 thru 23 give the distributions of σ_{zz} at $z = 0$ near the subcracks. In all cases the maximum values of σ_{zz} are near the main crack tip.

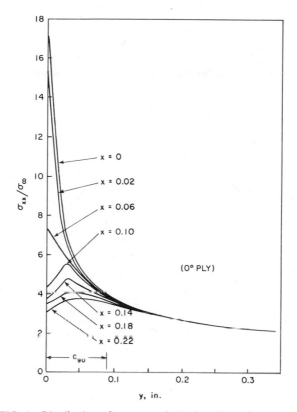

FIG. 4—*Distribution of* σ_{xx} *at* $z = h_0/2$ *along lines of constant* x.

Figure 23 indicates that σ_{zz} changes sign on lines of constant x as c_0 is crossed, and is discontinuous at c_0.

Discussion

Stress Redistribution Due to Subcracks

The stress distribution results for the sharp-crack problem with no sub-cracks indicated that the in-plane stresses followed the classical $\sqrt{r}$ singularity in the crack-tip region; the interlaminar stresses also increased rapidly as the crack tip was approached, in some cases after a sign reversal. When the subcracks are introduced into each ply in the present case, many stress components still tend to be higher near the main crack tip, but they are more distorted along the subcracks rather than simply centered at the main crack tip. Other stress components are forced to zero at the main crack tip due to the presence of the free edges of the subcracks.

The most important of the in-plane stresses in σ_{xx} is the 0° ply, as this eventually causes catastrophic failure when the fibers fail near the main

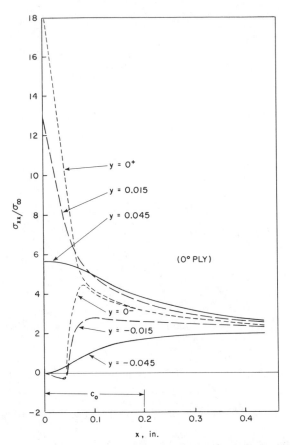

FIG. 5—*Distribution of σ_{xx} at z = $h_0/2$ along lines of constant y.*

crack tip [2, 4, 5]. Figure 24 compares the isostress contours of σ_{xx} in the 0° ply for the sharp-crack with and without subcracks. Figure 24 and the more precise discriptions in Fig. 4 and 5 indicate that the c_0 subcrack has the effect of greatly reducing the stress behind c_0 (for $y < 0$), while also reducing the very high values which normally would be reached just ahead of the main crack tip. Further away from the main crack tip, the stress is relatively unchanged from the sharp crack case.

An anticipated disturbance is produced in those cases where the introduction of the traction-free surfaces of c_0 and c_{90} require a particular stress component to be identically zero. Figures 7, 11, and 15 are such cases where the stress predictably increases rapidly from zero to some maximum value, and then decreases with further distance from the subcrack. Distributions of this type clearly give rise to interlaminar shear stresses which accomplish the stress-transfer process.

Another distinct group of curves is obtained for those cases where one

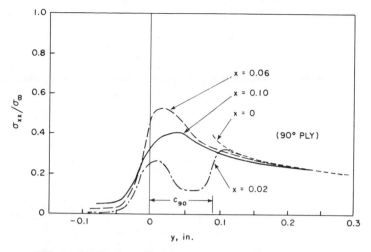

FIG. 6—*Distribution of σ_{xx} at $z = 3h_0/2$ along lines of constant x.*

ply is continuous over a subcrack in the adjacent ply. Figures 5, 6, 8, 9, 10, and 13 indicate that the in-plane stresses are continuous as the uncracked ply bridges across the cracked one. Curves of this type typically are well-behaved and usually show a maximum value at or near to the subcrack in the adjacent ply. Nontypical curves, such as the curve for $y = 0.015$ in Fig. 8, are obtained when the stress in question is plotted along lines very near to the subcrack free edge where the stress must be identically zero.

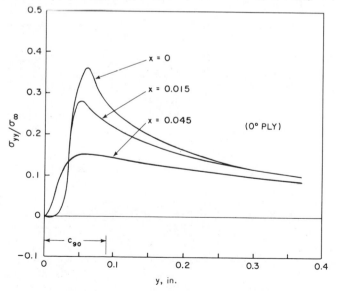

FIG. 7—*Distribution of σ_{yy} at $z = 0$ along lines of constant x.*

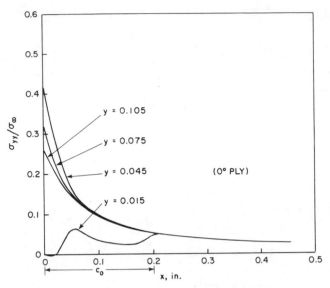

FIG. 8—*Distribution of* σ_{yy} *at* $z = h_0/2$ *along lines of constant* y.

The interlaminar stresses also are greatly disturbed by the presence of the subcracks. The interlaminar shear stresses are completely redistributed relative to the sharp-crack solution and are best described in terms of the mechanisms of stress transfer discussed in the next section. The interlaminar normal stress, σ_{zz}, responds to the disturbance in the other stress com-

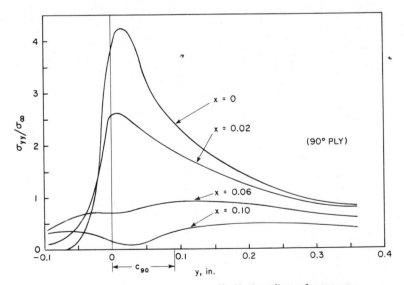

FIG. 9—*Distribution of* σ_{yy} *at* $z = 3h_0/2$ *along lines of constant* x.

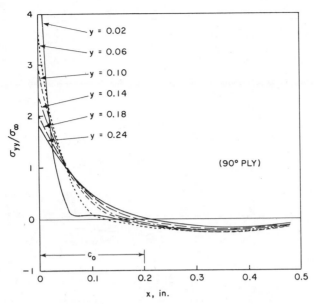

FIG. 10—*Distribution of σ_{yy} at $z = 3h_0/2$ along lines of constant y.*

ponents along the subcracks. Of greatest interest is Fig. 23, which indicates that σ_{zz} is discontinuous across c_0 and changes in sign from compressive on the crack flank side to tensile for $y > 0$. Apparently, this sign reversal is in response to the difference in σ_{xx} in the 0° ply on each side of c_0 (Fig. 5), while the stresses in the 90° ply are continuous across c_0; the degree of biaxiality of the in-plane stresses was found to have a significant effect on σ_{zz} in the sharp crack problem.

The introduction of subcracks c_0 and c_{90} also creates the suspicion of a potentially strong disturbance at the tip of each subcrack. However, no distribution resembling a singular subcrack tip stress field is evident in the results. Figures 6 and 9 describe σ_{xx} and σ_{yy} along the c_{90} subcrack flank region, and ahead of its tip. The stress parallel to the fibers of the 90° ply, σ_{yy}, shows no disturbance whatever in the subcrack tip region. The transverse stress, σ_{xx}, shows a very slight disturbance and rather irregular behavior along the extended subcrack flank. Similarly, σ_{xx} and σ_{xy} in Figs. 5 and 16 show no disturbance at the c_0 subcrack tip. Thus, the results for this case suggest a stress field centered at the main crack tip and distorted in response to the complex subcrack geometry, as distinct from a superposition of the main crack tip singular stress field with local subcrack singular stress fields. Stress transfer through adjacent, continuous plies along the subcracks apparently eliminates their stress-intensification potential, so that subcrack growth for a particular subcrack zone geometry may be treated by a local strength type of criterion rather than by a local brittle fracture criterion such as K_c.

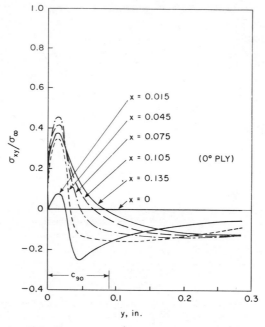

FIG. 11—*Distribution of σ_{xy} at $z = h_0/2$ along lines of constant* x.

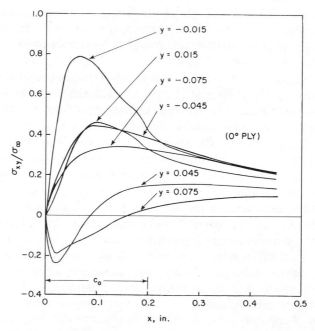

FIG. 12—*Distribution of σ_{xy} at $z = h_0/2$ along lines of constant* y.

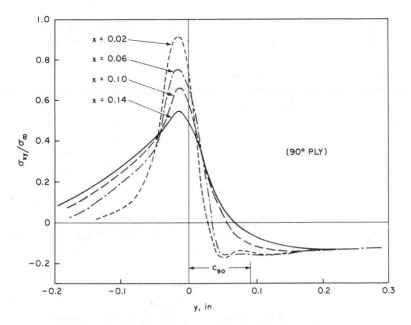

FIG. 13—*Distribution of* σ_{xy} *at* $z = 3h_o/2$ *along lines of constant* x.

Mechanisms of Stress Transfer

The distribution of certain stress components along the subcracks provides clarification of the mechanisms by which stress is transferred and concentrated ahead of the main crack. While several mechanisms of transfer may be understood intuitively, it is important to realize that less obvious effects such as coupling of the stress-transfer mechanics through the equilibrium equations also may play an important role. This discussion will consider only the more prominent mechanisms which act directly in the transfer of stress across the subcracks.

The mechanisms of stress transfer along c_o related to the displacement of the 0° ply indicated in Fig. 3 are of particular interest. Figure 5 elucidates the effects of stress transfer across c_o particularly well. Comparison of the $y = 0^+$ and $y = 0^-$ curves as a function of x indicates a severe discontinuity of σ_{xx} across c_o near the main crack tip. As the stress is transferred across c_o, the difference between the two curves decreases sharply until they are nearly identical at some point along the length of c_o, and finally the two curves join together at the tip of c_o. For the sharp-crack case, the 0^+ and 0^- curves would be identical everywhere. Figures 9 and 13 indicate the response of the in-plane transverse and shearing stresses of the adjacent 90° ply to the opening and in-plane shearing of the c_o subcrack (Fig. 3). Both stresses show a high peak as the 90° ply is stretched and sheared by the action of the $0°$ ply. The shearing action is of great significance in transferring σ_{xx} from one side of c_0 to the other through the interlaminar shear stress σ_{xz}.

The interlaminar stress distributions given in Figs. 17 thru 23 bear little resemblance to those obtained in the sharp-crack problem without subcracks. The distributions appear to be dominated by the subcracks and are explained logically in terms of the in-plane stress transfer effects which occur across the subcracks. All of the distributions are restricted to a region of several laminate thicknesses in extent on both sides of the subcracks. In each case the interlaminar shear stresses are plotted at the ply interface, where they are maximum.

The interlaminar shear stress σ_{yz} is generally lower than the other interlaminar stresses, but still it is important in transferring the in-plane stress σ_{yy} across the c_0 subcrack. In resisting the opening of c_0, the stress σ_{yy} must be transferred from the $90°$ ply to the $0°$ ply on each side of c_0 by σ_{yz}. Figure 17 shows the sign reversal in σ_{yz} on the two sides of c_0 as the $0°$ ply material is sheared in opposite directions of y in attempting to resist the opening of c_0.

Of more importance is σ_{xz}, which transfers the stress σ_{xx} across c_0, and enables the concentration of stress in the $0°$ ply ahead of the main crack tip, eventually resulting in catastrophic fracture. Figure 19 indicates the very high values of σ_{xz}, opposite in sign on each side of c_0. The mechanism of stress transfer which tends to concentrate the stress σ_{xx} ahead of the main crack tip may be described in a simple manner, ignoring coupling effects, as follows:

Upon application of the stress σ_∞, the main crack attempts to open, resulting in a shearing of one side of c_0 relative to the other side (Fig. 3).

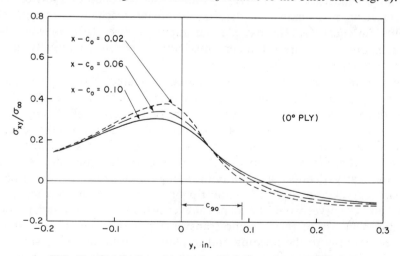

FIG. 14—*Distribution of σ_{xy} at $z = h_0/2$ along lines of constant x.*

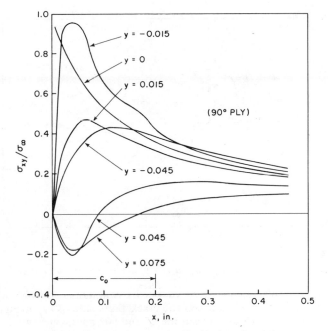

FIG. 15—*Distribution of σ_{xy} at z $=$ 3h$_0$/2 along lines of constant y.*

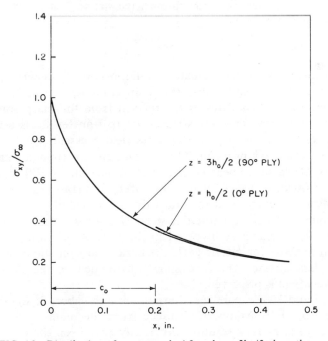

FIG. 16—*Distribution of σ_{xy} at z $=$ h$_0$/ 2 and z $=$ 3h$_0$/2 along the x-axis.*

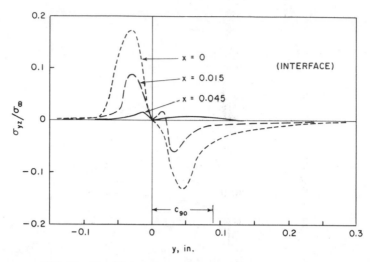

FIG. 17—*Distribution of* σ_{yz} *at* z = h₀ *along lines of constant* x.

This relative displacement is resisted by the continuous 90° ply, which crosses c_0 and is bonded to it. As the crack flank side of c_0 attempts to open, a stress σ_{xx} develops between the 0° and 90° plies, causing a strong response of σ_{xx} in the 0° ply, and a stress σ_{xy} in the 90° ply. The material in the 0° ply on the crack flank side of c_0 effectively pulls on the 0° material on the other side, primarily through the stress σ_{xy} in the 90° ply, which is transferred by σ_{xz}.

The Core Zone

The foregoing discussion indicates an important characteristic of the stress field: there is a region near the main crack tip, termed the "core zone," where the in-plane stresses are relaxed from the sharp-crack solution, and the interlaminar shear stresses act to transfer stress across the subcracks. Outside of this region the stress field is essentially the same as that for the sharp-crack problem. This characteristic is fundamental to the applicability of classical linear elastic fracture mechanics [12]. The traditional use of fracture mechanics for high-strength metals requires that the zone of plastic deformation at the crack tip be sufficiently small so that it is still surrounded by the $\sqrt{r}$ singular stress field of the elastic crack solution. While the mechanisms involved in the present solution are entirely different from those for metals [14], the basic characteristic of a zone of relaxed in-plane stresses, the core zone, surrounded by the classical $\sqrt{r}$ singular stress field is preserved.

Figures 25 and 26 compare the sharp-crack and subcrack solutions for σ_{xx}, σ_{yy}, and σ_{xy} as functions of distance from the main crack tip. The curves for the sharp-crack solution previously have been shown to follow the $\sqrt{r}$ singular behavior, as is evident by the slope of -1/2 of the curves on the log-log plots. The present solution, including subcracks, follows the identical $\sqrt{r}$ singularity outside of the core zone, then deviates to a more relaxed state inside it, similar to the expected behavior near a plastic zone in a metal. It should be noted that this behavior is observed despite the very large subcracks introduced, which are similar in length to the main crack.

The shape and size of the core zone varies between plies and in each direction due to the orthotropicity of the individual plies. The curves for $y = 0^+$ and 0^- in Fig. 5 give the best indication of the extent of the zone along c_0; the two curves almost merge at some point along c_0, and this could be regarded as the extent of the core zone along c_0 in the 0° ply. The interlaminar stress σ_{xz} in Fig. 20 also shows a distinct inflection at a similar point, and σ_{xy} in the 90° ply (Fig. 26) indicates a similar dimension. Figure 24 gives some indication of the core zone shape in various directions, but the exact size of the zone requires further investigation and possibly a finer finite-element mesh solution.

Figures 25 and 26 provide an accurate means for defining the core zone size; they also suggest the interesting result that the core zone size may be smaller than the c_0 and c_{90} subcracks. This may be related to the choice of the lengths of c_0 and c_{90} for this problem. Since the experimental evidence [5] indicates the existence of a small delamination zone which is not included in the analytical model, it is possible that either the splits would not extend as far without the delamination, if the interlaminar strength

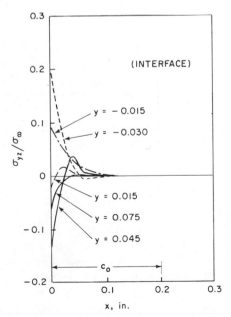

FIG. 18—*Distribution of σ_{yz} at $z = h_0$ along lines of constant y.*

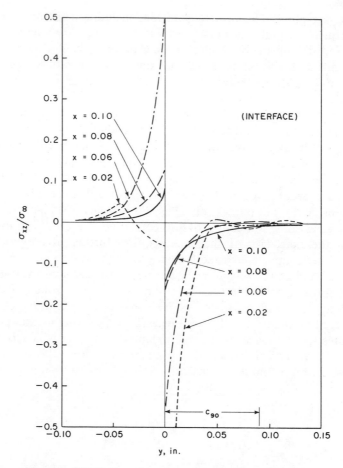

FIG. 19—*Distribution of* σ_{xz} *at* $z = h_0$ *along lines of constant* x.

were higher, or the zone would extend over a greater distance, in the presence of delamination. Further work is necessary to clarify the matter.

Significance of Core Zone Size

The relaxation of the crack-tip stress singularity due to the growth of subcritical cracks within the core zone is thought to be a major cause of the toughness achieved in composites of this type. The size of the core zone may be related to the fracture toughness of a given laminate configuration in much the same manner as is commonly employed in defining the toughness of metals [15]; available experimental evidence [5, 6] tends to support this view. If the material is altered by changing the ply thickness for example, the toughness may increase [5] if the zone is made larger or decrease if it is made smaller. The size of the c_0 and c_{90} subcracks observed

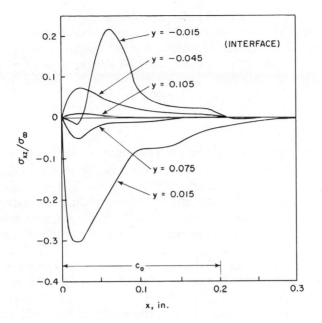

FIG. 20—*Distribution of σ_{xz} at $z = h_0$ along lines of constant y.*

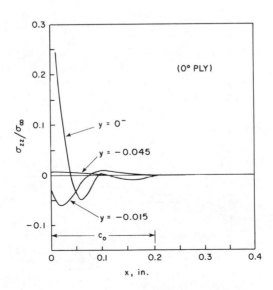

FIG. 21—*Distribution of σ_{zz} at $z = 0$ along lines of constant y, extending over the crack flank.*

in experiments may be a good indication of the effective core zone dimension. The growth of the zone may depend on the elastic ply properties and ply strengths, the subcrack topology, the ply thickness and stacking arrangement, the loading conditions, etc. Nonlinear aspects of the shear stress-strain curve also may significantly affect the results, particularly the distribution of σ_{xy} along c_o in the 90° ply.

Crack Length Correction for K_I

The critical stress intensity factor frequently is observed to vary with crack length and other specimen dimensions for engineering materials [6, 16, 17]. A common practice with metals has been to apply a crack length correction factor to account for the forward shift of the singular elastic stress field associated with the crack-tip plastic zone growth [15], and a similar approach has been employed for composites to account for size effects [3, 16].

The results given in Figs. 24 thru 26 for the present subcrack zone geometry indicate no forward shift in the singular stress field due to the introduction of the subcracks. Thus, although specimen size effects also have been reported for specimens of the type analyzed here [6], there is no apparent justification for the use of a crack length correction factor to rationalize the experimental observations. This does not preclude the meaningful use of such an approach for other subcrack zone geometries, such as occur in the case of angle-plied laminates, however.

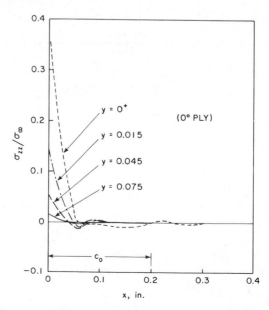

FIG. 22—*Distribution of σ_{zz} at $z = 0$ along lines of constant y.*

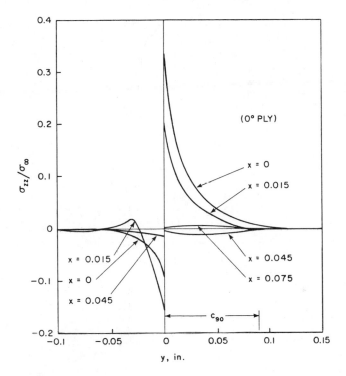

FIG. 23—*Distribution of σ_{zz} at $z = 0$ along lines of constant x.*

Subcrack Extensions

The extension of the subcracks c_0 and c_{90} does not appear to occur by a single fracture mode. Apparently, the stress field in the region of the subcracks is a complex combination of the main crack tip singularity and free-edge effects. The extension of c_0 and c_{90}, and possibly other splits and delaminations, must be considered as a local fracture problem which is different for each case, rather than a gross effect of the main crack extension mode.

As an example of the combined fracture mode problem, the extension of the c_0 subcrack will be considered. c_0 experiences a tendency to fracture under a combination of opening (Mode I), sliding (Mode II), and tearing (Mode III) with respect to the x-y plane. The opening mode originates from σ_{yy} in the 90° ply transferred above c_0, and σ_{yy} in the 0° ply at the tip of c_0. The sliding mode originates from σ_{xy} in the 90° ply over c_0 and σ_{xz} at the interface, which changes sign across c_0. The tearing mode originates from σ_{zz} which changes sign in crossing c_0. Also, an opening mode fracture of c_0 with respect to the x-z plane may be caused by σ_{yz} on both sides of c_0. Similar local stress fields tend to cause the extension of c_{90} by a combination of different modes.

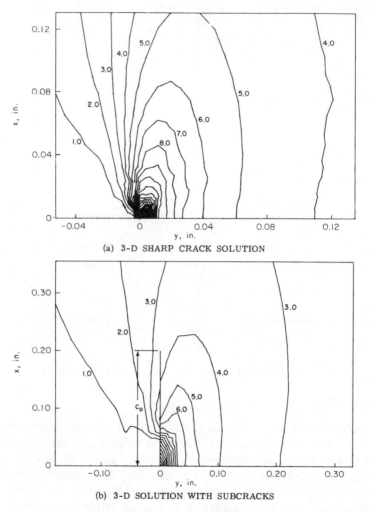

(a) 3-D SHARP CRACK SOLUTION

(b) 3-D SOLUTION WITH SUBCRACKS

FIG. 24—*Comparison of isostress contours of $\sigma_{xx}/\sigma_\infty$ in the $0°$ ply for the sharp crack with and without subcracks (note scale difference).*

The potential for the formation of additional subcracks and delaminations appears to be inherent in several of the stress distributions. The stress tending to form splits parallel to the fibers in the $0°$ and $90°$ plies shown in Figs. 6, 7, and 11 thru 13 suggest the formation of new subcracks in the range of several ply thicknesses ahead of the present subcracks, at the locations of the maxima in the curves. Such additional subcracks have been observed experimentally near these locations [4–6]. Figures 21 thru 23 show that σ_{zz} reaches high values along the right-hand side of c_0 and along c_{90}. This stress may produce a delamination region ahead of the crack tip in combination with σ_{xz} (Fig. 19). σ_{xz} also may produce some

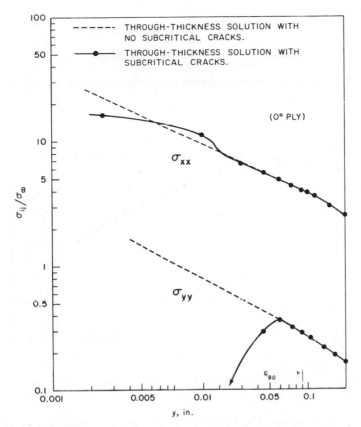

FIG. 25—*Comparison of σ_{xx} and σ_{yy} distributions of $z = h_0/2$ along the y-axis for solutions with and without subcracks.*

delamination behind c_0. Delamination zones of this general type, both ahead of and behind c_0, are described in Ref 5.

The stress levels reached in certain cases imply that some form of failure or nonlinear behavior is to be expected. Considering that the applied stress to obtain subcracks of these dimensions was experimentally in the range of 25 to 30 ksi, the shear stress σ_{xy} in the 90° ply over c_0 (Fig. 13) would be expected to become strongly nonlinear, and delamination due to σ_{xz} which reaches a value of 1.05 σ_∞ (Fig. 19) is to be expected. Local nonlinearity of σ_{xy} and delamination along c_0 would further alter the stress field and core zone dimension. Failure of the 0° ply due to σ_{xx} at the crack tip is also to be expected (Fig. 5) unless the effects of delamination and a nonlinear σ_{xy} serve to further reduce σ_{xx}, as could be anticipated.

Limitations of the Results

As in the case of the associated sharp-crack solution, the accuracy of the results is limited by the fineness of the finite element discretization. Thus,

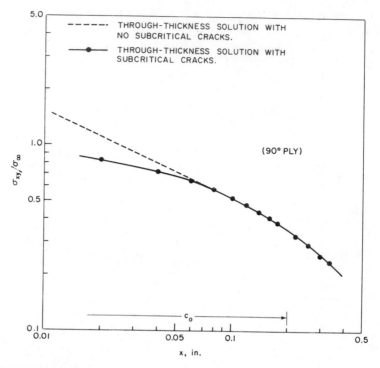

FIG. 26—*Comparison of* σ_{xy} *distributions at* z = 3h$_0$/2 *along the* x-*axis for solutions with and without subcracks.*

it is not possible to test the strength of the possible singularity, particularly of the interlaminar stresses, in regions arbitrarily close to the free edges and crack tip without a finer mesh solution. The results outside of these very localized regions are thought to be accurate, as discussed in greater detail in Ref 5. The finite element mesh used is thought to be sufficiently fine to allow a meaningful description of the mechanisms of stress transfer within the damage zone.

Conclusions

The stress field surrounding a sharp, through-thickness crack in a 0/90 laminate is severely changed by the introduction of subcracks parallel to the fibers of each ply. A core zone surrounding the main crack tip may be defined so that outside of the zone the singular stress field is undisturbed by the subcracks, while inside the zone the in-plane stress singularity is relaxed, and high levels of the interlaminar stresses are present. The mechanisms of stress transfer and stress concentration along the subcracks are identifiable, and mixed mode propagation of the subcracks is implied by the results. The subcracks appear to serve a function similar to the plastic zone in the case of a metal: the resistance to crack propagation is provided by a reduction of the singular in-plane stress field at the main crack tip. The relaxed core zone still is embedded in a singular stress field which is unaltered by the subcracks, indicating no foreward shift in the singular stress field.

Acknowledgment

This work was sponsored by the Air Force Materials Laboratory through Contract F33615-73-C-5169. The authors gratefully acknowledge this support.

References

[1] Cook, J. and Gordon, J. E., *Proceedings,* Royal Society (London), Vol. A282, 1964, p. 508.

[2] McGarry, F. J. and Mandell, J. F., "Fracture Toughness of Fibrous Glass Reinforced Plastic Composites," *Proceedings,* 27th Reinforced Plastic/Composites Div., Society of the Plastics Industry, Section 9A, 1972.

[3] McGarry, F. J. and Mandell, J. F., "Fracture Toughness Studies of Fiber Reinforced Plastic Laminates." *Proceedings, Special Discussion of Solid Solid Interfaces,* Faraday Division of the Chemical Society, Nottingham, England, 1972.

[4] Mandell, J. F., Wang, S. S., and McGarry, F. J., "Fracture of Graphite Fiber Reinforced Composites," Air Force Materials Laboratory Report AFML-TR-73-142, 1973.

[5] Mandell, J. F., Wang, S. S., and McGarry, F. J., "Fracture of Graphite Fiber Reinforced Composites," Air Force Materials Laboratory Report AFML-TR-74-167, 1974.

[6] Mandell, J. F., McGarry, F. J., Im, J., and Meier, U., "Fiber Orientation, Crack Velocity, and Cyclic Loading Effects on the Mode of Crack Extension in Fiber Reinforced Plastics," *Proceedings,* TMS/AIME Conference on Failure Modes in Composites II, Pittsburgh, Pa., 1974.

[7] Kelly, A., "Interface Effects and the Work of Fracture of a Fibrous Composite," *Proceedings,* Royal Society (London), A319, 1970, p. 95.

[8] Harrison, N. L., *Fiber Science and Technology,* Vol. 6, 1973, p. 25.

[9] Harrison, N. L., *Fiber Science and Technology,* Vol. 5, 1972, p. 197.

[10] Tirosh, J., *Journal of Applied Mechanics,* Transactions of the American Society of Mechanical Engineers, 1973, p. 785.

[11] Sih, G. C., Hilton, P. D., Badaliance, R., Shenberger, P. S., and Villarreal, G. in *Analysis of the Test Methods for High Modulus Fibers Composites, ASTM STP 521,* American Society for Testing and Materials, 1973, p. 98.

[12] Erdogan, F., "Fracture Problems in Composite Materials," NASA Technical Report NASA-TR-72-2, 1972.

[13] Sih, G. C., and Liebowitz, H. in *Fracture: An Advanced Treatise,* H. Liebowitz, Ed., Vol. 2, Academic Press, New York, 1968, p 67.

[14] Orowan, E. and Felbeck, D. K., "Experiments on Brittle Fracture of Steel Plates." *Welding Journal Supplement,* Nov. 1955.

[15] McClintock, F. A., discussion of "Fracture Testing of High Strength Sheet Materials," *Materials Research and Standards,* Vol. 1, 1961, p. 277.

[16] "Fracture Testing of High Strength Sheet Materials," First Report of Special *ASTM Bulltin,* Jan. 1960.

[17] Owen, M. J. and Bishop, P. J., *Journal of Composite Materials,* Vol. 7, 1973, p. 146.

S. N. Atluri,[1] A. S. Kobayashi,[2] and M. Nakagaki[1]

A Finite-Element Program for Fracture Mechanics Analysis of Composite Material

REFERENCE: Atluri, S. N., Kobayashi, A. S., and Nakagaki, M., "**A Finite-Element Program for Fracture Mechanics Analysis of Composite Material,**" *Fracture Mechanics of Composites, ASTM STP 593,* American Society for Testing and Materials, 1975, pp. 86–98.

ABSTRACT: An assumed displacement hybrid finite-element procedure developed for treating a general class of problems involving mixed-mode behavior of cracks is used to solve some two-dimensional, fracture mechanics problems involving rectilinear-anisotropic materials. This finite-element program uses four "singular" elements which surround the crack tip and "regular" elements which occupy the remaining region. The singular element has a built-in displacement field of the $\sqrt{r}$ type with the two modes of stress intensity factors, K_I and K_{II}, as unknowns. Displacement compatibility between singular and regular elements is also maintained. Isoparametric transformations are used to derive the stiffness matrix of quadrilateral curved elements. Rectilinear anisotropic, nonhomogeneous, but linear elastic, material properties are considered. The program was checked out by analyzing a bimaterial tension plate with an eccentric crack and a centrally-cracked orthotropic tension plate. The results thus obtained agreed well with those by Erdogan and Biricikoglu, and Bowie and Freese, respectively. The program was then used to analyze two fracture test specimens for which analytical solutions do not exist. The first specimen was the doubly edge-notched tension plate with material principal directions oriented 0°–90° or ±45° to the geometric axes of symmetry and with varying crack length. The second specimen was the three-point bend specimen with material principal directions oriented 0°–90° to the geometric axes of symmetry. Finally, an orthotropic tension plate with an oblique center crack was analyzed. Finite-element solutions of most of these problems do not seem to have appeared in prior literature.

KEY WORDS: fracture properties, stresses, composite materials, finite-element procedure, crack propagation, fatigue (materials)

Fracture studies of composite materials are much more complex than those of homogeneous, but brittle, engineering materials. In general, the

[1] Associate professor and post-doctoral fellow, respectively, School of Engineering Science and Mechanics, Georgia Institute of Technology, Atlanta, Ga. 30332.
[2] Professor, Dept. of Mechanical Engineering, University of Washington, Seattle, Wash. 98105.

singular state of stress surrounding the crack tip is not that of $1/\sqrt{r}$, and crack extension could be nonsymmetric despite the geometric symmetry of the problem. In addition, the possible presence of formation and coalescence of voids as well as craze formation in the singular region surrounding the crack tip distinguish the composite fracture from that of structural metals. Despite the complexity of the actual fracture process, the composite fracture should be dependent, to some extent, on the severity of the local singular state of stress which is governed by the strengths of singularity, K_1 and K_2.[3] These two quantities, which are the well-known stress intensity factors in linear fracture mechanics, should provide means of estimating the fracture load of a cracked composite material regardless of the failure criterion used. The purpose of this paper is to present a computational procedure by which the various physical quantities related to such a fracture criterion can be determined. For an up-to-date review of specific fracture criterion for composite materials as well as a summary of some of the known results published to date, the readers are referred to an excellent survey presented in Ref 1.[4]

The analytical difficulties in determining stress intensity factors in cracked homogeneous structures are compounded in composite materials because of the anisotropy and inhomogeneity of the materials involved. For composite materials, the limited analytical solutions of stress intensity factors for isotropic materials [2,3] are drastically reduced to a few problems with straight cracks in rectangular composite plates subjected to uniform loading conditions. The lack of even a handful of stress intensity factor solutions for different geometries and loading conditions makes it impossible to estimate stress intensity factors of real cracks in composite materials. It thus becomes imperative, in analyzing cracked composite material, to utilize the method of finite element analysis which has been used extensively to determine Mode I stress intensity factors as well as some mixed Modes I and II stress intensity factors in two-dimensional problems [4–9]. The simple computational procedure of using the crack opening displacement (COD) [4] or the computationally convenient procedure of using strain energy release rate [6,7] to estimate stress intensity factors, however, cannot be used to analyze cracked composite materials since the mixed modes of crack-tip deformation are more likely to co-exist in these problems. The finite-element procedure used in composite material analysis should therefore contain the proper singular state with stress intensity factors as unknowns which are to be determined together with the nodal forces and displacements.

In a recent paper, Tong and Pian [10] have shown that, for problems with singularities, the convergence rates of the finite-element method are

---

[3] K_1 and K_2 are defined as the stress intensity factors for a general singular state of stress $\sigma_{ij} \propto K/r^\alpha$ where α is not necessarily equal to $\frac{1}{2}$.

[4] The italic numbers in brackets refer to the list of references appended to this paper.

dominated by the singular nature of the solution near the crack tip. Thus, the order and format of stress singularities must be known a priori so that these singular stresses can be properly incorporated in the assumed functions in order to improve the rate of convergence. The special elements by Tracey [11] and Byskov [12] do not satisfy the inter-element boundary compatibility criteria and again, convergence of such a solution cannot be guaranteed, as has been proven by Tong and Pian [13].

To overcome these convergence problems, Pian, Tong, and Luk [9] used a special crack-tip finite element for isotropic materials with the correct singularities, of the $1/\sqrt{r}$ type for elastic analysis, in the assumed stresses of the hybrid finite-element model originated by Pian [14]. Parameters for the singular terms, together with the nodal displacements, are then solved from the final set of matrix equations. The magnitudes of singular terms, which are in fact the stress intensity factors K_I and K_II, are solved directly in this procedure. The results of Ref 9 have shown that the stress intensity factors for isotropic elastic material can be calculated accurately by using a much smaller number of degrees of freedom than by using only conventional elements.

Tong, Pian, and Lasry [15] have recently improved upon the analysis of Ref 9 by combining the hybrid element concept with those of the complex variable techniques developed by Bowie in his modified boundary collocation method for crack problems [16]. The proper $1/\sqrt{r}$ stress singularity was incorporated in the region surrounding the crack tip and led to very efficient programming. However, for anisotropic materials the complex variable formulation becomes somewhat complicated.

In this paper, application of a hybrid displacement model to two-dimensional problems in cracked composite material is presented. The discussion will be limited to the linear elastic, but arbitrary, anisotropic materials. The relative merits of the hybrid displacement method are presented.

Method of Approach

The mathematical formulation of the hybrid displacement model for analyzing cracked structures is described in detail in Refs 17 and 18 and will not be repeated here. Basically the variational principle which governs the assumed displacement hybrid model [19,20] is a modified principle of minimum potential energy. In a solution of an elasticity problem, the displacements u_i in the interior element, the inter-element boundary displacement, v_i, and the element surface traction, T_{Li}, are treated as unknown variables. The vanishing of the variation $\delta\pi$ in the modified minimum potential energy principle, for arbitrary variations in displacements, δu_i, in the element, for arbitrary δT_{Li} on inter-element boundaries, and for admissible δv_i on inter-element boundaries, results in the respective Euler equations:

(a) satisfaction of the local equilibrium equations in the element, V_m;

(b) values of interior displacements, u_i, at inter-element boundaries coincide with the inter-element boundary displacements v_i which are treated as independent unknowns; and

(c) finally, the boundary tractions T_{Li}, which are treated as independent unknowns in the present problem, coincide with the tractions $\frac{1}{2}E_{ijkl}(u_{k,l} + u_{l,k})v_j$ generated at inter-element boundaries by the functions u_i where v_j is the direction cosine of the element boundary, ∂V_m. Thus, it can be seen that the hybrid finite-element model enables one to choose element displacement functions that are completely arbitrary and need not satisfy the inter-element compatibility condition. This inter-element compatibility is enforced a posteriori by introducing the inter-element boundary displacement v_i as an independent variable and enforcing the constraint condition $v_i = u_i$ on ∂V_m. The boundary tractions T_{Li}, which are treated as independent variables in the present problem, can also be viewed mathematically as Lagrangean multipliers to enforce the constraint $v_i = u_i$.

In applying this model to cracked composite plates, the plate is divided into two regions: (a) a small but fixed region near the crack tip where the singular, near-field solution is predominant; and (b) a region away from the crack tip where the effect of the singularity is not felt. Assuming that the nature of this singularity is known, appropriate displacements corresponding to the singular stresses (of $1/r^a$ type, where a is not necessarily equal to $\frac{1}{2}$) are incorporated in the assumed approximate functions for u_i in the elements surrounding the crack tip as follows:

$$\{u_i\}_S = [U_R]\{\beta\} + [U_S]\begin{Bmatrix} K_{\mathrm{I}} \\ K_{\mathrm{II}} \end{Bmatrix} \equiv [U_R]\{\beta\} + [U_S]\{K_S\} \qquad (1)$$

where U_R are simple polynomials, β are unknown independent parameters, K_{I} and K_{II} are stress intensity factors for Mode I and Mode II crack-tip deformation, and U_S are known displacement functions for plane problems which yield the correct singular behavior for stresses and strains in linear elastic analysis. In the remainder of this paper, the stress singularity will be assumed to be of the $1/\sqrt{r}$ type although all discussions are applicable to other singularities of $1/r^a$ type.

An independent element boundary displacement, v_i, which is uniquely interpolated by displacements at the nodes along the boundary, is then assumed. Since these nodes are common for elements that share the common boundary, inter-element boundary displacement compatibility is thus ensured as mentioned previously. For the elements adjacent to the crack tip, a $\sqrt{r}$ type displacement behavior is built into the boundary displacement along element boundaries which pass through the crack tip. Details of this arrangement are given in Refs 17 and 18.

Finally, element boundary tractions (which can also be identified as Lagrangean multipliers in the present formulation) are assumed for a singular element. Since the assumed displacement, u_i, for the singular element contains a $\sqrt{r}$ type behavior, these displacements will generate singular boundary tractions of the $1/\sqrt{r}$ type along the boundary. Thus, for numerical accuracy in the present formulation, the assumed tractions, T_{Li}, for a *singular element* must also contain a $1/\sqrt{r}$ type behavior to be compatible with those generated by u_i. Again, further details of the actual construction of the singular and regular elements can be found in Refs 17 and 18.

Advantages of the Hybrid Displacement Model

1. The present formulation leads to matrix equations with nodal displacements and stress intensity factors as unknowns. Since inter-element displacement compatibility is satisfied, it is easy to establish mathematical convergence of the solution for nodal displacements as well as stress intensity factors. Details of numerical convergence studies have already been presented in Ref 18.

2. Since the displacement along the boundary of a quadrilateral element in the present hybrid formulation is quadratic in nature, these quadrilateral elements are automatically "compatible" with similar quadrilateral elements with quadratic boundary displacements, but derived through the common (compatible displacement) finite-element model. Thus, the stiffness matrix for the four singular elements derived from the present procedure can be first assembled and then merged into the stiffness matrix for the remainder of the structure obtained through the more common displacement finite-element method. Since inter-element compatibility is still maintained, earlier arguments about convergence still apply.

3. Since boundary tractions for each element are introduced as independent variables in the present formulation, it is easy to satisfy any stress-free conditions, especially on the crack surface. This is done by simply assuming zero tractions in the formulation, on boundary segment of the element where such conditions should exist. Thus, stress-free conditions are satisfied a priori in the present formulation, as opposed to these conditions becoming the natural boundary conditions of the variational principle in the usual displacement formulation. In the hybrid stress formulation of Ref 9, such stress-free boundary conditions are also enforced a priori by properly choosing the stress field within each element such that it generates zero tractions on any segment of the boundary. Such a procedure becomes tedious for arbitrary quadrilateral elements that may

have curved boundaries. An accurate satisfaction of the stress-free conditions is shown to be mandatory for the numerical performance of the hybrid stress model in Ref 9.

4. Since element boundary displacements are assumed independently, it is an easy task to assume boundary displacements along boundaries of elements that share the crack tip as a node, such that they have the correct variation with respect to radial distance ($\sqrt{r}$ in the present analysis).

5. In evaluating the strain energy density integrals for singular elements, where in the assumed displacement field involves a combination of regular polynomial and $\sqrt{r}$ types of behavior, it can be seen that one encounters three types of integrands: (a) products of regular type tensors, (b) products of singular stress tensor ($1/\sqrt{r}$ type) and singular strain tensor of $1/\sqrt{r}$ type, and (c) product of regular stress tensor and singular strain tensor. It can be shown easily that, since the asymptotic solution for the singular stress tensor near the crack tip is self-equilibrated, by employing the divergence theorem and proper variable transformations, integrals of types (b) and (c) can be converted to boundary integrals free from singularities. Thus, the problem of having to numerically integrate singular integrals is avoided.

6. Available solutions for plastic yielding near the crack tip suggest that, in the limit of perfect plasticity, there may be singularities in strains but only finite stresses. Thus, construction of the hybrid displacement element near the crack tip that has proper strain singularities, but finite stress, appears attractive. The hybrid stress formulation, on the other hand, appears more complicated for such plasticity problems, and has not been attempted so far.

Applications

Center Crack in a Bimaterial Tension Plate

The legend in Fig. 1 shows the geometry, loading conditions, and finite element breakdown for the case of an eccentric crack in a bimaterial tension plate. Each of two materials was considered as homogeneous and isotropic. The theoretical solution for the corresponding infinite plate problem was given by Erdogan and Biricikoglu [21]. The problem was considered as one of plane strain and the load intensities σ_1 and σ_2 (Fig. 1) were considered to be related as $(1 - \nu_1^2) \sigma_1/E_1 = (1 - \nu_2^2) \sigma_2/E_2$. There are three singular points in the present problem: the two crack tips and the interface point. The nature of stress singularities, as seen from the referenced theoretical solution, are of $1/\sqrt{r}$ type near the crack tips and $1/r^\alpha$ type (where α depends on material properties) near the interface point. The latter built-in singularity at the interface point is $1/r^{0.273692}$

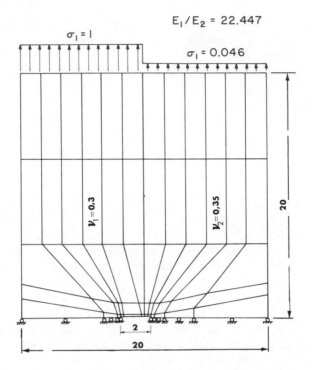

FIG. 1—*Finite-element breakdown of a bimaterial tension plate with an eccentric crack.*

in stresses. Because of symmetry, only one half of the plate is used in the present finite-element analysis. A total of 60 quadrilateral elements with 215 nodes were employed. In the present analysis, a total of six singular elements are used: two each at the above-mentioned singular points. The calculated values of the four stress intensity factors are given in the following:

	K_1 (Material 1)	K_2 (Material 2)	K_θ (Interface)	K_r (Interface)
Present	1.459 σ_1	2.890 σ_2	$-0.116\ \sigma_1$	0.0093 σ_1
Erdogan and Biricikoglu [21]	1.375 σ_1	2.767 σ_2	$-0.119\ \sigma_1$	0.0437 σ_1

Thus, there is an error of about 6 percent in K_1, and an error of 4.5 percent in K_2. However, the stress-intensity factors at the interface are in errors of over one-hundred percent. Attempts were not made at the refinement of the finite element grid to study to rate of convergence of the present solution to that given in the referenced report.

Center Crack Orthotropic Tension Plate

Accuracy of the developed procedure was assessed by analyzing a centrally-cracked orthotropic tension plate and by comparing the obtained results with the analytical solution by Bowie and Freese [22]. Stress intensity factors in this and subsequent figures (except Fig. 6) are presented in non-dimensional form. The presented results can thus be scaled provided the material properties remain identical. Principal directions of the orthotropic material were aligned in the two lines of symmetry and therefore only one quadrant of the plate was considered in this analysis. The legend in Fig. 2 shows the 24-element and 93-node quadrant used in this analysis. The material properties being considered are: ratios of modulus of elasticity, E_x/E_y = 0.3, 0.7, 1.0, 1.5, and 4.5, and the computed variations in stress intensity factors are shown in terms of the ratios of modulus of elasticity. An excellent agreement between the results of finite-element analysis and that of Bowie and Freese is noted.

Double Edge-Cracked Tension Plate

The legend in Fig. 3 shows element and nodal breakdown of two orthotropic double-edge-cracked tension specimens with two aspect ratios of 4

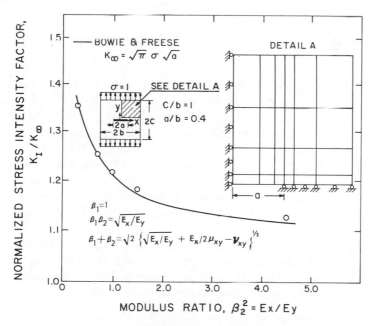

FIG. 2—*Stress intensity factor in an orthotropic tension plate with central crack.*

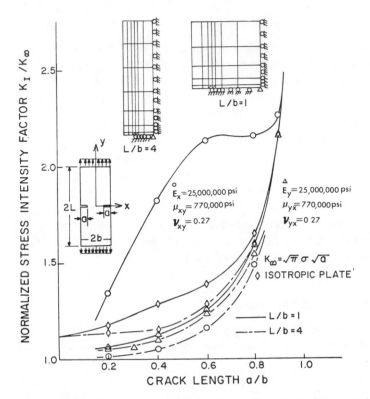

FIG. 3—*Stress intensity factor in an orthotropic tension plate with double external cracks. Material principal directions parallel to geometric axes of symmetry.*

and 1, respectively. The material properties[5] were held constant in this case and the crack depth was varied from 0.2 to 0.8 of half-specimen width. Figure 3 shows the variation in stress intensity factor with variation in crack depth for two orientations of the principal directions of orthotropic material properties. Noticeable differences in the stress intensity factor with difference in aspect ratios are noted for the material which is very rigid in longitudinal direction. Also noted are the stress intensity factors for shorter crack length which are significantly lower than the theoretical values of 1.12 for isotropic double-edge-notched tension plate with short cracks.

The legend in Fig. 4 shows the element and nodal breakdown of the same double-edge-cracked tension plate but with the principal direction oriented ±45° to the geometric axis of symmetry. Due to the antisymmetry of the problem, the entire plate had to be used in finite-element analysis

---

[5] The material properties shown in Figs. 4 and 5 relate to carbon epoxy laminate with parallel ply at 0 and 90 deg and angle ply at ±45 deg.

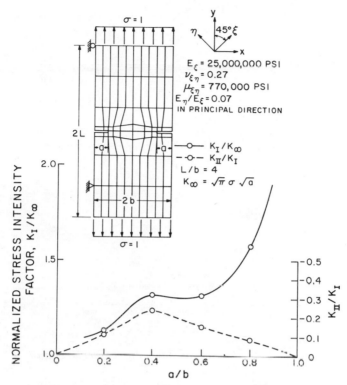

FIG. 4—*Stress intensity factor in an orthotropic tension plate with double external cracks. Material principal directions 45° to geometric axes of symmetry.*

thus increasing the number of elements and nodes to 80 and 103, respectively. Obviously, the same nodal breakdown can be used for arbitrary orientation of the principal axes of the material. Figure 4 shows the variation in stress intensity factor with variation in crack length for $E_{+45°}/E_{-45°} = 14.285$. These stress intensity factors do not differ substantially from those shown in Fig. 3. The large values of K_{II}, however, indicate the influence of the orientation of the reinforcing fibers in the material.

Three-Point Bend Specimen

The legend in Fig. 5 shows element and nodal breakdowns of a three-point bend specimen composed of orthotropic materials. Again, the material properties[6] were held constant and the stress intensity factors were computed for crack depth from 0.4 to 0.8 of specimen width for two

[6]The material properties shown in Figs. 4 and 5 relate to carbon-epoxy laminate with parallel ply at 0 and 90 deg and angle ply at ±45 deg.

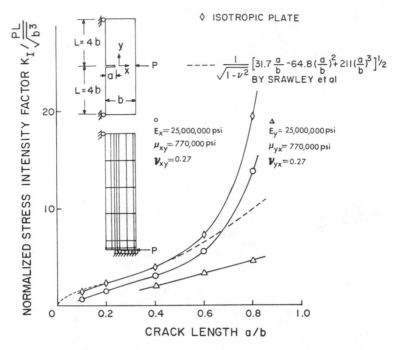

FIG. 5—*Stress intensity factor in an orthotropic three-point bend specimen.*

orientations of principal directions of the material properties. Figure 6 also shows a comparison of the computed stress intensity factor and that by Srawley et al [23] for an isotropic material.

Orthotropic Tension Plate with Slanted Crack

The legend in Fig. 6 shows element nodal breakdown of an orthotropic tension plate with a crack inclined at 45° to the direction of loading (*y*-axis). The principal directions of orthotropy are the *x* and *y*-axes. Because of geometrical asymmetry, the entire plate was analyzed, which involved 96 elements and 260 nodes. The finite-element solutions for the stress intensity factors were obtained as: $K_I = 1.0195$ and $K_{II} = 1.0759$. The available solution for an orthotropic infinite plate by Sih, Paris, and Irwin [24] suggests that $K_I = K_{II} = 1.0539$. Thus, the calculated value for K_I for the present finite plate is about 3 percent lower than the theoretical value for the infinite plate, where as the computed K_{II} is about 2 percent higher than the corresponding theoretical value for the infinite plate. It is interesting to note, however, that for a similar case of an isotropic plate with a slanted crack, Wilson [25] has found that K_I is higher and K_{II} is lower than the corresponding theoretical solutions.

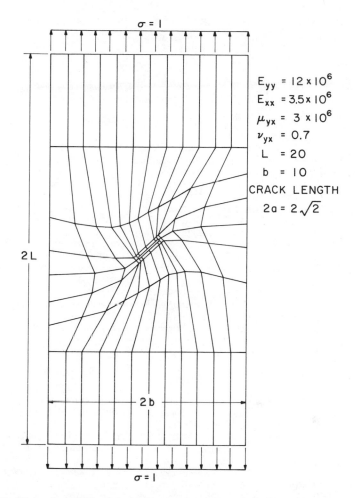

FIG. 6—*Finite-element breakdown in an orthotropic tension plate with a slanted crack.*

Conclusion

The validity of an assumed displacement hybrid finite-element procedure, in calculating stress intensity factors for two-dimensional fracture problems involving composite materials, is established. Several new results for cracks running through dissimilar media, double-edge cracks in orthotropic tension specimens for different orientations of principal axes of orthotropy, different crack depths, and different crack orientations have been presented.

Acknowledgments

This work was supported by the Air Force Office of Scientific Research under grant AFOSR-73-2478 and 74-2667. The encouragement received from W. J. Walker is gratefully appreciated.

References

[1] Erdogan, F., *Engineering Fracture Mechanics,* Vol. 4, 1972, pp. 811–840.

[2] Tada, H., Paris, P., and Irwin, G., *The Stress Analysis of Cracks Handbook,* Del Research Corporation, Hellertown, Pa., 1973.

[3] Sih, G. C., *Handbook of Stress Intensity Factors,* Institute of Fracture and Solid Mechanics, Lehigh University, Bethlehem, Pa., 1973.

[4] Kobayashi, A. S., Maiden, D. E., Simon, B. J., and Iida, S., "Application of the Method of Finite Element Analysis to Two-Dimensional Problems in Fracture Mechanics," ASME Paper No. 69-WA/PVP-12.

[5] Chan, J. K., Tuba, I. S., and Wilson, W. K., *Journal of Engineering Fracture Mechanics,* Vol. 2, 1970, pp. 1–17.

[6] Watwood, V. B., *Nuclear Engineering and Design,* Vol. II, 1969, pp. 323–332.

[7] Anderson, G. P., Ruggles, V. L., and Stikor, G. S., *International Journal of Fracture Mechanics,* Vol. 7, No. 1, March 1971, pp. 63–76.

[8] Hilton, P. D. and Sih, G. C. in *Methods of Analysis of Crack Problems,* G. C. Sih, Ed., Noordhoff International Publishing, Leyden, 1973, pp. 426–483.

[9] Pian, T. H. H., Tong, P., and Luk, C. H., "Elastic Crack Analysis by a Finite Element Hybrid Method," *Proceedings,* Third International Conference on Matrix Methods in Structural Mechanics, Wright-Patterson AFB, Ohio, Nov. 1971.

[10] Tong, P. and Pian, T. H. H., *International Journal of Solids and Structures,* Dec. 1973, pp. 313–321.

[11] Tracey, D. M., *International Journal of Fracture Mechanics,* Vol. 3, No. 3, 1971, pp. 255–266.

[12] Byskov, E., *International Journal of Fracture Mechanics,* Vol. 6, No. 2, June 1970, pp. 159–167.

[13] Tong, P. and Pian, T. H. H., *International Journal of Solids and Structures,* Vol. 3, 1967, pp. 865–879.

[14] Pian, T. H. H., "Element Stiffness Matrices for Boundary Compatibility and for Prescribed Boundary Stresses," *Proceedings,* First Conference of Matrix Methods in Structural Mechanics, AFFDL-TR-66-80, 1967, pp. 457–477.

[15] Tong, P., Pian, T. H. H., and Lasry, S., "A Hybrid-Element Approach to Crack Problems in Plane Elasticity," to appear in the *International Journal of Numerical Methods in Engineering.*

[16] Bowie, O. L. and Neal, D. M., *International Journal of Fracture Mechanics,* Vol. 6, 1970, pp. 299–306.

[17] Atluri, S., Kobayashi, A. S., and Nakagaki, M., "Application of an Assumed Displacement Hybrid Finite Element Procedure to Two-Dimensional Problems in Fracture Mechanics," AIAA Paper No. 74-390, *AIAA/ASME/SAE 15th Structures, Structural Dynamics and Materials Conference,* Las Vegas, 17–19 April 1974.

[18] Atluri, S., Kobayashi, A. S., and Nakagaki, M., *International Journal of Fracture,* Vol. 11, No. 2, April 1975, pp. 257–271.

[19] Tong, P., *International Journal of Numerical Methods in Engineering,* Vol. 2, 1970, pp. 78–83.

[20] Atluri, S. and Pian, T. H. H., *Journal of Structures and Mechanics,* Vol. 1, No. 1, 1972, pp. 1–43.

[21] Erdogan, F., and Biricikoglu, V., "Two Bonded Half Planes with a Crack Going Through the Interface," NASA-TR-72-4, June 1972.

[22] Bowie, O. L. and Freese, C. E., *International Journal of Fracture Mechanics,* Vol. 8, March 1972, pp. 49–58.

[23] Srawley, J. E. and Brown, W. R., *Fracture Toughness Testing and Its Applications, ASTM STP 381,* American Society for Testing and Materials, 1965, pp. 133–196.

[24] Sih, G. C., Paris, P., and Irwin, G., *International Journal of Fracture Mechanics,* Vol. 1, 1965, pp. 189.

[25] Wilson, W. K., *Journal of Basic Engineering,* Transactions of ASME, Series D, Vol. 93, No. 4, 1971, pp. 685–690.

H. J. Konish, Jr.[1]

Mode I Stress Intensity Factors for Symmetrically-Cracked Orthotropic Strips

REFERENCE: Konish, H. J., Jr., **"Mode I Stress Intensity Factors for Symmetrically-Cracked Orthotropic Strips,"** *Fracture Mechanics of Composites, ASTM STP 593,* American Society for Testing and Materials, 1975, pp. 99–116.

ABSTRACT: The effects of material anisotropy on the stress intensity factor are investigated numerically for both double-edge-cracked and center-cracked orthotropic tensile strips. The material properties employed correspond to homogeneous material models of mid-plane symmetric fiber composite laminates of varying ply orientation and ply properties.

The effects of anisotropy are found to be dependent on both specimen geometry and material properties. Complete decoupling of these geometric and material influences does not appear possible. However, the principal geometric parameter seems to be the distance from the crack tip to the free edge of the specimen; the effects of material properties appear to correlate with the in-plane elastic shear modulus. It is suggested that anisotropic effects can be sufficiently controlled, by means of specimen geometry, to justify the use of the known isotropic stress intensity factor as a reasonable (and usually conservative) *estimate* of the anisotropic value in most materials.

KEY WORDS: fracture properties, composite materials, stresses, crack propagation

A basic concept of linear elastic fracture mechanics is that the singular elastic stress field induced by a sharp crack may be completely characterized by the stress intensity factor (SIF). Calculation of the SIF is thus a central element of fracture mechanics. Accurate determination of the SIF is particularly important in fracture testing, where the value of the stress characterization at the onset of unstable crack growth in the test piece is regarded as a material property. However, exact closed-form expressions for the SIF can be analytically determined only under rather limited conditions.

[1] NRC research associate, Nonmetallic Materials Division, Air Force Material Laboratory, Wright-Patterson AFB, Ohio 45433; presently, senior engineer, Advanced Reactors Division, Westinghouse Electric Corp., Madison, Pa. 15663.

A typical example is that of an infinite two-dimensional homogeneous body, subjected to Mode I loading and containing a single straight crack (Fig. 1). The SIF for this problem, denoted by K_I, is [1][2]

$$K_I = \sigma_0 \sqrt{\pi a} \qquad (1)$$

where σ_0 is the applied tensile stress, and a is half of the crack length.

It is noted that Eq 1 is independent of material properties, being equally applicable to materials which are isotropic (for example, metallic alloys) and to those which are anisotropic with the plane of the problem (for example, mid-plane symmetric fiber composite laminates) [1].

The geometric model used to obtain Eq 1 can never be completely realized in an experimental form, and even a close approximation of the model can be obtained only with very large plate specimens containing relatively small cracks. However, fabrication and testing of such specimens are both difficult and expensive. These practical considerations have led to the use of smaller specimens, in which the test piece dimensions and the implanted

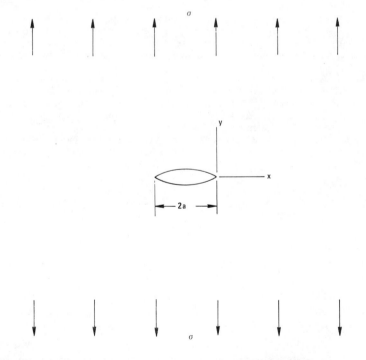

FIG. 1—*One-dimensional crack in a plane subjected to remote uniform tension transverse to the crack (Mode I loading).*

[2] The italic numbers in brackets refer to the list of references appended to this paper.

crack are of comparable size. Clearly, Eq 1 is not directly applicable to these smaller specimens, as it contains no provision for characterizing the interaction between the crack tip and the external boundaries of the specimen. These effects may be introduced, in an empirical fashion, by modifying Eq 1 to the form

$$K_I = \sigma_0\, Y\sqrt{a} \tag{2}$$

where Y, the K-calibration factor, reflects the influence of specimen geometry on the SIF. Values of Y have been obtained, using experimental and numerical techniques, for a number of typical fracture test configurations [1, 2]. The resulting K-calibration factors are appropriate for fracture test specimens of any isotropic material.

Material anisotropy introduces an additional degree of complexity to the problem of calculating the SIF for fracture test specimens. As in the isotropic case, Eq 1 must be modified to account for the effects of specimen geometry. In the anisotropic case, however, it appears that material properties also influence the SIF[3–5]. Thus, the strictly geometric K-calibration factor does not completely specify the modifications necessary to apply Eq 1 to anisotropic test specimens; some characterization of material properties is also required.

An assessment of the effects of material anisotropy on the SIF in symmetrically-cracked tensile strips, based on a numerical investigation of two distinct specimen configurations and a variety of materials, is reported herein. The materials considered, all of which are orthotropic with respect to the natural coordinate systems of the specimens, represent typical midplane symmetric fiber composite laminates. The results presented in this report indicate that the influence of anisotropic material properties on the SIF is closely coupled with that of specimen geometry. Although complete separation of these two effects is not achieved, a governing parameter can be tentatively identified for each effect. It is also observed that the effects of material anisotropy can be significantly reduced, often to negligible levels, by careful specimen design.

Analysis

A uniquely appropriate numerical analysis method [3], based on the boundary-integral formulation of the plane elasticity problem [6–8], was used to obtain the results reported herein. The basic character of the boundary-integral solution technique is retained in the present implementation, in that only the specimen boundaries must be modeled as a collection of discrete segments; however, the present version differs from its predecessors in that the existence of a sharp crack is implicit in the formulation of the problem. Consequently, it is not necessary to model the actual crack boundary, but only the portion of the specimen boundaries exclusive of the crack. The significant problems of accuracy and model size associated with discrete segment models of sharp cracks are thereby avoided. An additional advantage of the implicit crack formulation is that the SIF at the crack tip may be directly calculated; the necessity of inferring this value by extrapolating stress and/or displacement data back to the crack tip is thus eliminated. As presently formulated, the solution technique is convenient to use and very accurate; however, as with most numerical analysis methods, some experience is necessary to extract the maximum potential of the program.

The analysis method was applied to two specimen configurations, the double-edge-cracked tension (DEC) specimen, and the center-cracked tension (CCT) specimen (Fig. 2). The crack length was variable for each configuration, ranging from 10 to 70 percent of the specimen width in 10 percent increments. Changes in crack length did not, of course, require alteration of the boundary segment models, as no physical representation of the crack itself is necessary (Fig. 3 and 4). However, it was necessary to model each configuration separately, since the numerical method is formulated for a single straight crack, centered at the origin, and aligned with the x-axis. Thus, 2 deg of implicit symmetry could be specified for the CCT model, but, although both specimen configurations are equally symmetric, the DEC model had only 1 deg of implicit symmetry. The second axis of symmetry for the DEC model was obtained by applying appropriate conditions on the model boundary corresponding to the centerline of the specimen (Fig. 3)

The materials investigated were mid-plane symmetric fiber composite laminates, all of which were orthotropic with respect to the specimen axes. These laminates were modeled as linear elastic homogeneous materials, in accordance with lamination theory [9]. Primary emphasis was focused on angle-ply laminates of Narmco T300/5208 graphite/epoxy, as they constitute the simplest class of orthotropic laminates. However, since angle-ply laminates are not representative of the materials typically used in real structures, a selection of more complex laminates was included in the study. A variety of material systems was employed in this portion of the work. Elastic ply properties of the different fiber/matrix material systems considered in the study are listed in Table 1.

Uniform displacement boundary conditions were used to simulate fixed-grip loading (Figs. 3 and 4). The tractions induced by the applied displacements were averaged to obtain a value of applied stress. Except in the case of the unidirectional (0° specimens, these tractions are quite uniform (within 7 percent of the average value); moreover, this uniformity is essentially insensitive to changes in crack length. Thus, in most instances, the specimen length appears sufficient to eliminate any end effects on the SIF. Though such end effects do exist in the (0°) specimens, no attempt was made to

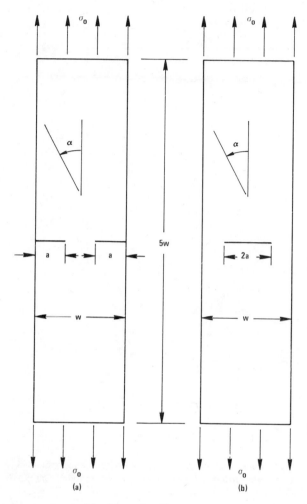

FIG. 2—*Specimen types used in this study. The two specimen geometries differ only in the placement of the crack.*

either eliminate the traction variation or to correct the average traction value.

The analysis was performed using a CDC 6600 computer. Because of the large number of boundary segments used in the specimen models, the solution times were relatively large, being approximately 190 s for a DEC specimen and 110 s for a CCT specimen. Recent results have indicated that solution times may be significantly reduced, with little or no loss in accuracy, by using fewer and larger boundary segments away from the vicinity of the crack.

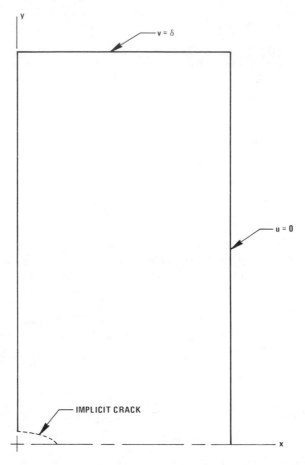

FIG. 3—*Model of one quarter of the double-edge-cracked fracture specimen. Displacement boundary conditions are used to impose symmetry and induce load. The x-axis is a line of implicit symmetry and, like the crack boundary, is not modeled.*

Results

For each combination of specimen type, crack length, and laminate, values of K_1 and σ_0 were numerically obtained. The isotropic K-calibration factor Y is also known for each specimen type, as a function of relative crack length [2]. It is convenient to introduce an additional parameter H, the anisotropy factor, which is defined as the ratio of the anisotropic SIF to its isotropic counterpart

$$H = K_1/\sigma_0 Y\sqrt{a} \tag{3}$$

The deviation of H from its isotropic value of unity is a direct measure of the influence of material anisotropy on the SIF.

FIG. 4—*Model of one quarter of the center-cracked fracture specimen. Displacement boundary conditions are used for loading. The coordinate axes are lines of implicit symmetry; like the crack boundary, they are not modeled.*

Values of H for the angle-ply materials investigated are listed numerically in Tables 2 and 3, and shown graphically in Figs. 5 and 6. These results indicate that the anisotrophy factor is a function of both material properties and specimen configuration. The relationship between H and each of these two variables is considered separately.

The effect of variable crack length on H is markedly different in the two types of specimens; the influence of material anisotropy increases with crack length in the CCT specimens and decreases with crack length in the DEC specimens. This behavior may be explained by noting that, since Eq 1 is valid for both isotropic and anisotropic materials, the influence of anisotropy on the SIF must result from interaction between the local stress field surrounding the crack tip and the external boundaries

TABLE 1—*Ply Properties.*

Narmco T300/5208 graphite epoxy[a]
$$E_{11} = 20.5 \times 10^6 \text{ lb/in.}^2$$
$$E_{22} = 1.37 \times 10^6 \text{ lb/in.}^2$$
$$G_{12} = 0.752 \times 10^6 \text{ lb/in.}^2$$
$$\nu_{12} = 0.31$$

Boron/epoxy[b]
$$E_{11} = 30.0 \times 10^6 \text{ lb/in.}^2$$
$$E_{22} = 2.7 \times 10^6 \text{ lb/in.}^2$$
$$G_{12} = 0.65 \times 10^6 \text{ lb/in.}^2$$
$$\nu_{12} = 0.21$$

HTS graphite/epoxy[b]
$$E_{11} = 21.0 \times 10^6 \text{ lb/in.}^2$$
$$E_{22} = 1.7 \times 10^6 \text{ lb/in.}^2$$
$$G_{12} = 0.65 \times 10^6 \text{ lb/in.}^2$$
$$\nu_{12} = 0.28$$

E-glass/epoxy[b]
$$E_{11} = 5.6 \times 10^6 \text{ lb/in.}^2$$
$$E_{22} = 1.2 \times 10^6 \text{ lb/in.}^2$$
$$G_{12} = 0.60 \times 10^6 \text{ lb/in.}^2$$
$$\nu_{12} = 0.26$$

[a] Private communication, J. R. Eisenmann, General Dynamics Corporation, Fort Worth, Tex., 1973.
[b] Halpin, J. C., Jerina, K. L., and Johnson, T. A., in *Analysis of the Test Methods for High Modulus Fibers and Composites, ASTM STP 521,* American Society for Testing and Materials, 1973, pp. 5–64.

TABLE 2—*Anisotropy factor in DEC angle-ply specimens of T300/5208 graphite/epoxy.*

$2a/W$[a] α[a]	0.1 H	0.2 H	0.3 H	0.4 H	0.5 H	0.6 H	0.7 H
$(0°)_s$	0.945	0.956	0.965	0.972	0.979	0.986	0.991
$(\pm 10°)_s$	0.969	0.978	0.984	0.987	0.991	0.994	0.996
$(\pm 15°)_s$	0.992	0.999	1.002	1.003	1.003	1.002	1.001
$(\pm 20°)_s$	1.019	1.024	1.026	1.023	1.019	1.013	1.008
$(\pm 25°)_s$	1.050	1.052	1.055	1.049	1.041	1.029	1.018
$(\pm 30°)_s$	1.083	1.082	1.086	1.079	1.066	1.049	1.031
$(\pm 35°)_s$	1.120	1.115	1.112	1.107	1.092	1.069	1.043
$(\pm 45°)_s$	1.142	1.148	1.135	1.131	1.116	1.087	1.057
$(\pm 55°)_s$	1.112	1.122	1.116	1.098	1.084	1.064	1.048
$(\pm 60°)_s$	1.092	1.097	1.089	1.072	1.058	1.045	1.036
$(\pm 65°)_s$	1.056	1.067	1.059	1.045	1.035	1.027	1.023
$(\pm 70°)_s$	1.022	1.037	1.029	1.021	1.016	1.013	1.012
$(\pm 75°)_s$	0.996	1.008	1.005	1.002	1.001	1.002	1.004
$(\pm 80°)_s$	0.973	0.985	0.986	0.987	0.990	0.994	0.998
$(90°)_s$	0.947	0.960	0.967	0.973	0.981	0.987	0.993

[a] See Fig. 2a.

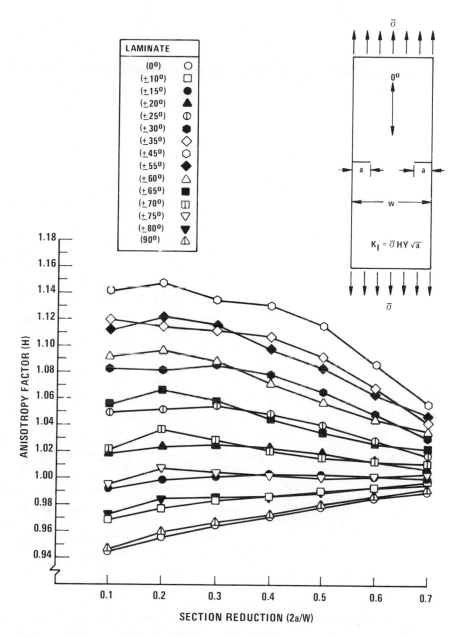

FIG. 5—*Anisotropy factor versus net section reduction for double-edge-cracked specimens.*

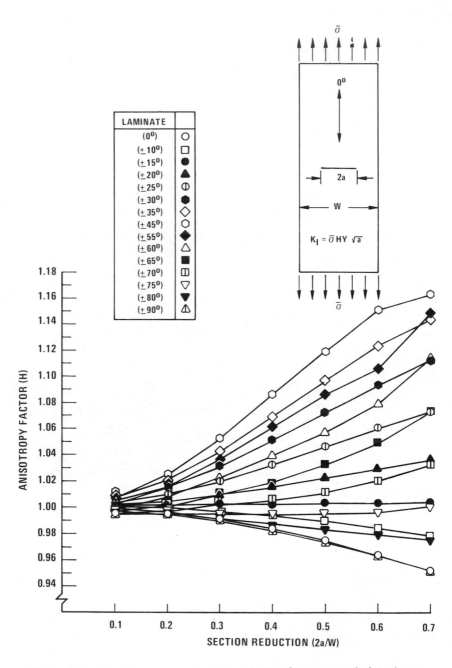

FIG. 6—*Anisotropy factor versus net section reduction for center-cracked specimens.*

TABLE 3—*Anisotropy factor in CCT angle-ply specimens of T300/5208 graphite/epoxy.*

$2a/W^a$ α^a	0.1 H	0.2 H	0.3 H	0.4 H	0.5 H	0.6 H	0.7 H
$(0°)_s$	1.000	0.997	0.991	0.984	0.975	0.964	0.952
$(\pm 10°)_s$	1.001	1.000	0.997	0.994	0.990	0.985	0.979
$(\pm 15°)_s$	1.002	1.002	1.003	1.003	1.004	1.004	1.005
$(\pm 20°)_s$	1.003	1.005	1.010	1.016	1.023	1.030	1.037
$(\pm 25°)_s$	1.004	1.010	1.020	1.033	1.047	1.061	1.074
$(\pm 30°)_s$	1.005	1.016	1.032	1.052	1.073	1.094	1.113
$(\pm 35°)_s$	1.007	1.021	1.043	1.070	1.098	1.125	1.145
$(\pm 45°)_s$	1.007	1.025	1.053	1.087	1.120	1.152	1.164
$(\pm 55°)_s$	1.002	1.016	1.037	1.062	1.087	1.107	1.149
$(\pm 60°)_s$	0.999	1.008	1.023	1.040	1.058	1.080	1.115
$(\pm 65°)_s$	0.996	1.002	1.010	1.020	1.033	1.050	1.073
$(\pm 70°)_s$	0.995	0.997	1.001	1.006	1.012	1.021	1.034
$(\pm 75°)_s$	0.995	0.995	0.995	0.995	0.996	0.997	1.002
$(\pm 80°)_s$	0.996	0.995	0.992	0.988	0.984	0.980	0.976
$(90°)_s$	0.998	0.995	0.990	0.983	0.974	0.964	0.952

"See Fig. 2b.

of the specimen. The anisotropy factor may thus be interpreted as a measure of the extent to which such interactions occur. This interpretation suggests that the effects of anisotropy should increase as the crack tip approaches a specimen boundary. It follows that the relationship between the anisotropy factor and crack length will be dependent on specimen type; a more useful correlation is obtained by relating H to ℓ_f, the free-edge distance, which is simply the distance from the crack tip to the specimen edge. The free-edge distance is not independent of specimen type, being the crack length

$$\ell_f = a \qquad (4)$$

in DEC specimens, and the uncracked ligament length

$$\ell_f = W/2 - a \qquad (5)$$

in CCT specimens.

The relationship between the anisotropy factor and the free-edge distance, for both CCT and DEC specimens of several representative angle-ply laminates, is shown graphically in Fig. 7. For a given laminate, the anisotropy factor exhibits reasonably good correlation with free-edge distance, regardless of specimen type. The slight disparity observed between specimen types at small values of ℓ_f is attributed to the differing orientation of the crack, relative to the specimen edge, in the two configurations. At small values of ℓ_f, these differing crack orientations may well cause variations in the interaction between the specimen edge and the

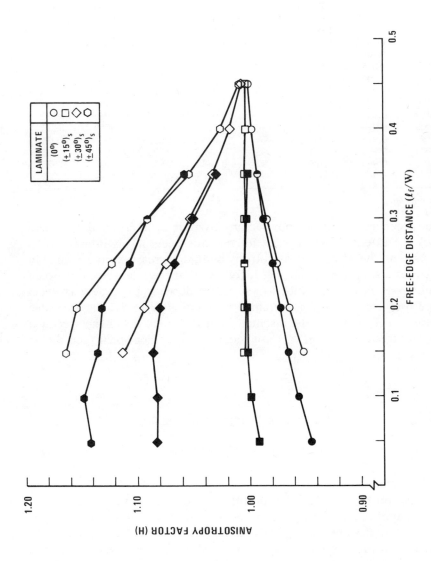

FIG. 7—*Anisotropy factor versus free-edge distance for representative laminates. Open points denote center-cracked specimens; filled points denote double-edge-cracked specimens.*

crack-tip stress field. The distinction between specimen types does diminish as ℓ_f increases. This seeming convergence may, however, be due to the fact that anisotropy factors, regardless of specimen type and material, approach a common limit of unity for sufficiently large values of ℓ_f. Although the exact influence of specimen type on the anisotropy factor has not been resolved, specimen configuration does appear to be of secondary importance to free-edge distance.

The relationship between material properties and the anisotropy factor must also be considered. Regardless of specimen type and crack length, the effect of anisotropy on the SIF is most severe for a $(\pm 45°)_s$ laminate; the anisotropic effects decrease from this maximum in very nearly symmetric fashion, for both increasing and decreasing ply angles (Figs. 5 and 6). This behavior suggests a correlation between the anisotropy factor and G_{xy}, the in-plane laminate shear modulus. A physical basis for this correlation may also be suggested, as the mode of load transfer around the crack is expected to be quite sensitive to changes in the laminate shear modulus. However, G_{xy} is not a completely satisfactory parameter, since it varies with both laminate orientation and ply properties; a more suitable variable is $\overline{G}$, the relative shear modulus, which is the shear modulus of the laminate in question divided by the shear modulus of a $(0°/\pm 45°/90°)_s$ quasi-isotropic laminate of the same fiber/matrix material system. Thus, a value of $\overline{G}$ greater than unity indicates a laminate which is relatively stiff in shear; a value of $\overline{G}$ less than unity indicates a laminate which is relatively soft in shear.

The relationship between the anisotropy factor and the relative shear modulus, for both DEC and CCT specimens of angle-ply materials, is shown graphically in Figs. 8 and 9. Each point shown represents the average of the two anisotropy factors for a given specimen configuration, corresponding to the two angle-ply laminates having the same shear modulus. The error involved in this averaging procedure is quite small, the actual data typically falling within the symbol used to denote the average value.

The data shown in Figs. 8 and 9 may be fitted with a set of bilinear curves, each of which corresponds to a single specimen type and free-edge distance. The curves shown are simply fitted to the data visually, and thus are not optimal representations of the data in a least-squares sense; the data do, however, fit the curves reasonably well. It is interesting to note that each bilinear curve breaks at a single value of $\overline{G}$, corresponding to isotropic material properties. The response of the anisotropy factor to changes in material properties thus appears to be divided into two regimes, according to whether the relative shear modulus is greater or less than unity. Within each regime, H may be closely approximated as a linear function of $\overline{G}$. A fundamental explanation of this behavior requires further investigation of the details of load transfer around the crack.

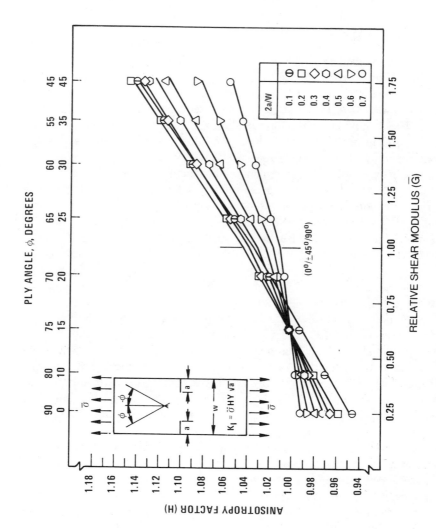

FIG. 8—*Anisotropy factor versus relative shear modulus for double-edge-cracked specimens.*

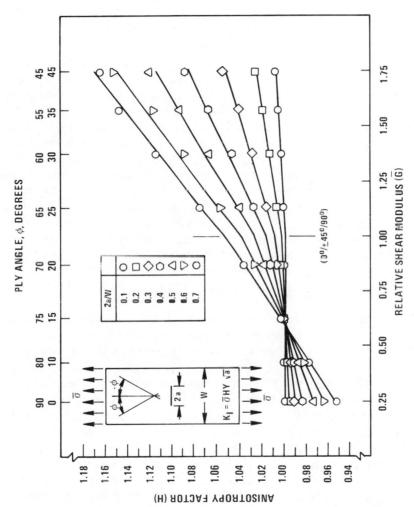

FIG. 9—*Anisotropy factor versus relative shear modulus for center-cracked specimens.*

Discussion

The results presented here indicate that the SIF in an anisotropic fracture specimen differs from the corresponding isotropic value by an amount which depends on both specimen geometry and material properties. Of course, manipulation of these same test parameters provides some degree of control over the severity of anisotropic effects on the SIF. Thus, the anisotropic effects can be reduced to such an extent that the isotropic SIF may be an acceptable characterization of the specimen, simply by judicious prescription of fracture test procedures.

The most manageable test parameters are those of specimen geometry, that is, specimen type and free-edge distance. The influence of the latter parameter is easily assessed, as it is shown that the effects of anisotropy on the SIF increase significantly as the crack tip approaches the free edge of the specimen. However, the very small free-edge distances considered in this study are not typical of conventional fracture test specimens, where ℓ_f is usually no less than 25 percent of the specimen width. The anisotropic SIF is then within 12 percent of its isotropic counterpart. Of course, the difference between the two SIF values may well be less than 12 percent which is an upper bound on approximation error. Moreover, for most angle-ply laminates, the isotropic SIF yields a conservative value of fracture strength; in those cases where the isotropic estimate is not conservative, the difference between the isotropic and anisotropic values of the SIF is relatively small. Thus, a lower bound on free-edge distance may be sufficient to justify the use of the isotropic SIF as an *estimate* of the anisotropic value.

The significance of specimen shape must also be considered in evaluating the effects of material anisotropy on the SIF. The doubly-symmetric specimens considered in this work are expected to be more susceptible to the effects of anisotropy than are specimens having only 1 deg of in-plane symmetry (for example, single-edge-cracked specimens, loaded in either tension or bending). This expected difference between specimen types is attributed to bending effects in the less symmetric specimens, which lead to more severe stress gradients near the crack tip. Consequently, the crack is relatively more dominant in singly-symmetric specimens, and the influence of material properties would then be reduced. The widespread use of singly-symmetric specimen geometries for fracture testing of fiber composites suggests further investigation of the relationship between specimen shape and the influence of anisotropy on the SIF.

It should also be noted that the results presented here are restricted to angle-ply laminates. In the mixed orthotropic laminate constructions more typically encountered in aircraft structures, some reduction of anisotropic influences may occur simply because the mixed laminates are less directional than are the angle-plies. This hypothesis is supported by some preliminary results covering a number of mixed orthotropic laminates of several fiber/matrix material systems. These results are shown as anisotropy factors for both CCT and DEC specimen types in Tables 4 and 5. These data suggest that the influence of material anisotropy on the SIF is significantly less in mixed orthotropic laminates than in angle-ply constructions. Further investigation of this area is certainly indicated.

TABLE 4—*Anisotropy factor in DEC specimens of mixed orthotropic laminates.*

α Material $2a / W^a$	$(0°/ \pm 45°)_s$ HTS H	$(0°_2/ \pm 45°)_s$ Boron / Epoxy H	$(0°_2/ \pm 45°)_s$ HTS H	$(0°_2/ \pm 45°)_s$ Glass / Epoxy H	$(0°_4/ \pm 45°)_s$ HTS H
0.1	1.040	1.010	1.010	1.003	0.997
0.2	1.037	1.012	1.012	1.004	0.992
0.3	1.037	1.014	1.014	1.006	0.995
0.4	1.033	1.013	1.013	1.006	0.997
0.5	1.030	1.014	1.014	1.008	1.001
0.6	1.018	1.007	1.006	1.003	0.998
0.7	1.011	1.004	1.004	1.002	0.998

^{a} See Fig. 2a.

TABLE 5—*Anisotropy factor in CCT specimens of mixed orthotropic laminates.*

α^a Material $2a / W$	$(0°/ \pm 45°)_s$ HTS H	$(0°_2/ \pm 45°)_s$ Boron / Epoxy H	$(0°_2/ \pm 45°)_s$ HTS H	$(0°_2/ \pm 45°)_s$ Glass / Epoxy H	$(0°_4/ \pm 45°)_s$ HTS H
0.1	1.002	1.002	1.002	1.001	1.001
0.2	1.006	1.003	1.003	1.001	1.001
0.3	1.012	1.005	1.005	1.002	1.000
0.4	1.019	1.008	1.008	1.003	0.999
0.5	1.028	1.011	1.011	1.004	0.998
0.6	1.037	1.014	1.014	1.005	0.996
0.7	1.045	1.017	1.017	1.006	0.994

^{a} See Fig. 2b.

Conclusions

The effects of material anisotropy on the SIF in symmetrically-cracked tension specimens of orthotropic materials are shown to be significant in some instances. The severity of anisotropic effects is a function of both material properties and specimen geometry. The anisotropic effects can be sufficiently reduced, by controlling specimen geometry, to justify using the isotropic SIF as an estimate of the anisotropic value. The isotropic estimate is usually conservative; nonconservative estimation errors are very small.

The particular combination of symmetrically-cracked tension specimens and angle-ply laminates appears to maximize the influence of material anisotropy. Less symmetric specimen geometries and mixed orthotropic laminates are both expected to reduce anisotropic effects, though further investigation of both of these areas is required. However, present data suggest that the isotropic SIF may be cautiously employed as an *estimate* of the anisotropic value.

Acknowledgments

This work was performed during the author's tenure as a National Research Council Research Associate at the Air Force Materials Laboratory. The research opportunity provided by this appointment is deeply appreciated. Equally appreciated are the efforts of T. A. Cruse, who provided the computer program used in this study, and much valuable advice on the use of that program.

References

[1] Paris, P. C. and Sih, G. C. in *Fracture Toughness Testing and Its Applications, ASTM STP 318,* American Society for Testing and Materials, 1965, pp. 30–81.

[2] Brown, W. F., Jr. and Srawley, J. E., *Plane Strain Crack Toughness Testing of High Strength Metallic Materials, ASTM STP 410,* American Society for Testing and Materials, 1967, pp. 8–16.

[3] Snyder, M. D. and Cruse, T. A., "Crack Tip Stress Intensity Factors in Finite Anisotropic Plates," AFML-TR-73-209, Air Force Materials Laboratory, Air Force Systems Command, Wright-Patterson AFB, Ohio, 1973.

[4] Bowie, O. L. and Freese, C. E., *International Journal of Fracture Mechanics,* Vol. 8, 1972, pp. 49–58.

[5] Cruse, T. A., and Osias, J. R., "Exploratory Development on Fracture Mechanics of Composite Materials," AFML-TR-74-111, Air Force Materials Laboratory, Air Force Systems Command, Wright-Patterson AFB, Ohio, 1974, pp. 34–101.

[6] Cruse, T. A. in *The Surface Crack: Physical Problems and Computational Solutions,* The American Society of Mechanical Engineers, 1972, pp. 153–170.

[7] Cruse, T. A. and Van Buren, W., *International Journal of Fracture Mechanics,* Vol. 7, 1971, pp. 1–15.

[8] Cruse, T. A. in *Proceedings,* International Conference on Variational Methods in Engineering, Southampton University, England, 1973, pp. 9.1–9.29.

[9] Ashton, J. E., Halpin, J. C., and Petit, P. H., *Primer on Composite Materials: Analysis,* Technomic Publishing Co., Inc., Stanford, Conn., 1969, pp. 1–58.

R. J. Nuismer[1] and J. M. Whitney[2]

Uniaxial Failure of Composite Laminates Containing Stress Concentrations

REFERENCE: Nuismer, R. J. and Whitney, J. M., **"Uniaxial Failure of Composite Laminates Containing Stress Concentrations,"** *Fracture Mechanics of Composites, ASTM STP 593,* American Society for Testing and Materials, 1975, pp. 117–142.

ABSTRACT: Two previously developed failure criteria for predicting the uniaxial tensile strength of a laminated composite containing through-the-thickness material discontinuities (notches) are subjected to further experimental scrutinization. In particular, the two-parameter (unnotched tensile strength of the laminate and a characteristic length) models, which are capable of predicting observed discontinuity size effects without resorting to the concepts of linear elastic fracture mechanics, are based on limited experimental verification.

In the present paper, and experimental program is presented which examines the effect of changes in the material system, the laminate fiber orientations, and the notch shape and size (stress gradient), on the model predictions. This is accomplished by obtaining experimental data on two material systems, glass/epoxy and graphite/epoxy, in conjunction with two orientations of fiber-dominated laminates containing through-the-thickness circular holes and sharp tipped cracks of several sizes.

In addition to the test results, two observations based on the models are presented. First, the statistical failure distribution for a composite containing a circular hole is predicted using the models and shown to agree well with experimental observations. Second, an Irwin type correction factor applied to the stress intensity factor is shown to result in nearly constant values of the critical stress intensity factor for all values of crack length. The correction factor is shown to be related to the characteristic length of the present models.

KEY WORDS: fracture properties, composite materials, stresses, laminates, fracture strength, failure, notch strength

Because of their importance in design applications, laminated, continuous-fiber reinforced-resin matrix composites containing through cutouts have been the subject of considerable study, for example, see Refs *1* thru *4*.[3] In

---

[1] Assistant professor, Department of Mechanical Engineering, University of Utah, Salt Lake City, Utah 84112.

[2] Materials research engineer, Mechanics and Surface Interactions Branch, Nonmetallic Materials Division, Air Force Materials Laboratory, Wright-Patterson AFB, Ohio 45433.

[3] The italic numbers in brackets refer to the list of references appended to this paper.

the course of this study, attention was called to a phenomenon that has since become known as the "hole size effect," that is, for tension specimens containing various sized circular cutouts, larger holes cause greater strength reductions than do smaller holes.

Noting that this effect could not be explained by a classical stress concentration factor approach (all sized holes have the same stress concentration factor), an attempt [1] was made to explain the phenomenon by using linear elastic fracture mechanics (LEFM). In this approach [1], the hole was modeled as having two slits extending symmetrically from either side of the hole, perpendicular to the direction of load application. Although called intense energy regions, the slits were modeled mathematically as cracks via the Bowie crack solution [5]. Then, knowing the critical stress intensity factor, K_Q, from an independent fracture test, and the length of the intense energy region, a, from the results of a test on a laminate containing a particular hole size, the strength of a laminate containing *any* hole size could be predicted provided the length, a, remained constant for all hole sizes in that particular laminate. It was shown in Ref *1* that the model served to predict the proper trend of tensile strength reduction with increased hole size. Furthermore, the model was shown to result in a reasonable quantitative correlation with available data.

Although the application of LEFM concepts to laminates containing circular cutouts understandably produced an increased interest in the use of fracture mechanics with composite laminates, the need for such concepts is not entirely clear. This is because of the following two observations [6]: (1) single cracks of the type observed in metals do not form in resin matrix composites under repeated loads; and (2) unlike metals, a positive correlation between the unnotched tensile strength of a composite and its fracture toughness seems to exist, that is, the greater the tensile strength the greater the fracture toughness. In view of these observations, the question arises as to the necessity of LEFM concepts for either the design or materials characterization of laminated composites.

With these facts in mind, another explanation of the hole size effect was introduced in Ref 7. Here, the explanation was based simply on the difference that exists in the normal stress *distribution* ahead of a hole for different sized holes, as shown for an isotropic material in Fig. 1. It is seen that, although all sized holes have the same stress concentration factor, the normal stress perturbation from a uniform stress state is considerably more concentrated near the hole boundary in the case of the smaller hole. Thus, intuitively, one might expect the plate containing the smaller hole to be the stronger of the two, since a greater opportunity exists in this case to redistribute high stresses. Through cracks were also considered in Ref 7, where it was found that the crack size effect on measured values of fracture toughness (the variation of measured fracture toughness with crack size [8]) could be explained in a similar manner by considering the *exact* elasticity solution

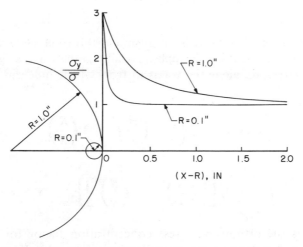

FIG. 1—*Normal stress distribution for a circular hole in an infinite isotropic plate.*

for the normal stress ahead of a crack rather than just the singular term of the asymptotic expansion, see Fig. 2.

In addition to qualitatively explaining the observed size effects, remarkably good quantitative predictions of failure strengths were obtained using either of two models based on the normal stress distribution, as described in Ref 7. Although the predictions were limited to holes in glass/epoxy and cracks in graphite/epoxy, the excellent correlation between theory and experiment in these two cases raised the question of whether the model might not be a useful design tool for predicting failure strengths of notched composites in general. In the present paper, the results of an experimental program designed to help answer this question are presented.

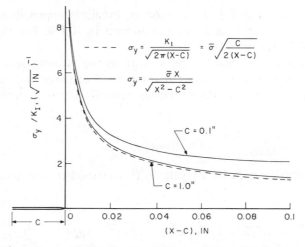

FIG. 2—*Normal stress distribution for a center crack in an infinite anisotropic plate.*

Failure Criteria

Consider a hole of radius R in an infinite orthotropic plate, as shown in Fig. 1. If a uniform stress, σ, is applied parallel to the y-axis at infinity, then the normal stress, σ_y, along the x-axis in front of the hole can be approximated by

$$\sigma_y(x, 0) = \frac{\bar{\sigma}}{2}\left\{2 + \left(\frac{R}{x}\right)^2 + 3\left(\frac{R}{x}\right)^4\right.$$

$$\left. - (K_T^\infty - 3)\left[5\left(\frac{R}{x}\right)^6 - 7\left(\frac{R}{x}\right)^8\right]\right\}, \qquad x > R \tag{1}$$

where K_T^∞ is the orthotropic stress concentration factor for an infinite width plate as determined from the following relationship [9]

$$K_T^\infty = 1 + \sqrt{\frac{2}{A_{22}}\left(\sqrt{A_{11}A_{22}} - A_{12} + \frac{A_{11}A_{22} - A_{12}^2}{2A_{66}}\right)} \tag{2}$$

where A_{ij} are the in-plane laminate stiffnesses as determined from laminated plate theory [10]. The Subscript 1 denotes the direction parallel to the applied stress at infinity. In terms of effective elastic moduli, denoted by a bar, Eq 2 becomes

$$K_T^\infty = 1 + \sqrt{2\left(\sqrt{\frac{\bar{E}_{11}}{\bar{E}_{22}}} - \nu_{12}\right) + \frac{\bar{E}_{11}}{\bar{G}_{12}}} \tag{3}$$

Eq 1 was shown in Ref 11 to provide an excellent approximation to the exact orthotropic plate solution as contained in Ref 9. For the isotropic case ($K_T^\infty = 3$), the expression is exact.

The first failure criterion [7], referred to as the "point stress criterion," assumes failure to occur when σ_y at some fixed distance, d_0, ahead of the hole first reaches the *unnotched* tensile strength of the material, σ_0, that is, when

$$\sigma_y(x, 0)|_{x=R+d_0} = \sigma_0 \tag{4}$$

Using this criterion with Eq 1 results in the notched to unnotched strength ratio

$$\frac{\sigma_N^\infty}{\sigma_0} = 2/\{2 + \xi_1^2 + 3\xi_1^4 - (K_T^\infty - 3)(5\xi_1^6 - 7\xi_1^8)\} \tag{5}$$

where

$$\xi_1 = R/(R + d_0) \tag{6}$$

and σ_N^∞ equals the notched strength of the infinite width laminate that is, the applied stress, $\bar{\sigma}$, at failure. Note that for very large holes, $\zeta_1 \to 1$, the classical stress concentration result, $\sigma_N^\infty/\sigma_0 = 1/K_T^\infty$, is recovered. On the other hand, for vanishingly small hole sizes, $\xi_1 \to 0$, the ratio $\sigma_N^\infty/\sigma_0 \to 1$, as would be expected. Thus, the expected limits are found.

The second alternative failure criterion [7], called the "average stress criterion," assumes failure to occur when the average value of σ_y over some fixed distance, a_0, ahead of the hole first reaches the *unnotched* tensile strength of the material, that is, when

$$\frac{1}{a_0} \int_R^{R+a_0} \sigma_y(x, 0)\,dx = \sigma_0 \tag{7}$$

Using this criterion with Eq 1 results in the notched to unnotched strength ratio

$$\frac{\sigma_N^\infty}{\sigma_0} = 2(1 - \xi_2)/\{2 - \xi_2^2 - \xi_2^4 + (K_T^\infty - 3)(\xi_2^6 - \xi_2^8)\} \tag{8}$$

where

$$\xi_2 = R/(R + a_0) \tag{9}$$

and σ_N^∞ is again the *notched* strength of the infinite width laminate. It is easily shown that the expected limits of σ_N^∞/σ_0 are again recovered for very small and very large holes.

Considering the center cracked geometry of Fig. 2, the *exact* anisotropic elasticity solution for the normal stress ahead of a crack of length $2c$ in an infinite anisotropic plate under uniform uniaxial tension, σ, is given by [9]

$$\sigma_y(x, 0) = \frac{\sigma x}{\sqrt{x^2 - c^2}} = \frac{K_1 x}{\sqrt{\pi c(x^2 - c^2)}}, \qquad x > c \tag{10}$$

where K_1 is the stress intensity factor, which in this case is given by $K_1 = \sigma\sqrt{\pi c}$. Using this result with each of the failure criteria, Eqs 4 and 7 (with R replaced by c) yields, respectively

$$\frac{\sigma_N^\infty}{\sigma_0} = \sqrt{1 - \xi_3^2} \tag{11}$$

where

$$\xi_3 = c/(c + d_0) \tag{12}$$

and

$$\frac{\sigma_N^\infty}{\sigma_0} = \sqrt{\frac{1 - \xi_4}{1 + \xi_4}} \tag{13}$$

where

$$\xi_4 = c/(c + a_0) \tag{14}$$

The predicted crack size effect on the measured value of the fracture toughness, K_Q, can more easily be observed by writing Eqs 11 and 13 in the form

$$K_Q = \sigma_0\sqrt{\pi c(1 - \xi_3^2)} \tag{15}$$

$$K_Q = \sigma_0\sqrt{\pi c(1 - \xi_4)/(1 + \xi_4)} \tag{16}$$

respectively. These equations result from Eqs 11 and 13 simply by noting that $K_Q = \sigma_N^\infty\sqrt{\pi c}$ for the infinite plate geometry being considered. In both Eqs 15 and 16, the expected limit of $K_Q = 0$ for vanishingly small crack lengths is reached, while for large crack lengths, K_Q asymptotically approaches a constant value. For the point and average stress criteria, these asymptotic values are, respectively

$$K_Q = \sigma_0\sqrt{2\pi d_0} \tag{17}$$

$$K_Q = \sigma_0\sqrt{\pi a_0/2} \tag{18}$$

At this point, several comments concerning the models should be made. First, Eqs 5, 8, 15, and 16 all predict the proper trends of observed behavior, that is, decreasing strength of a laminate with increasing hole size and increasing fracture toughness with increasing crack size.

Second, it is clear that these equations are quite useless unless the characteristic distance, d_0 or a_0, remains constant for all hole or crack sizes in at least a particular laminate of a particular material system. In such a case, one test on one hole or crack size would allow the failure strength of that laminate containing any hole or crack size to be predicted. It is also clear that the utility of the model would be greatly increased if d_0 or a_0 were shown to remain constant for *all* laminates of a particular material system, and an even greater utility would be achieved if they were shown to remain constant for *all* laminates of *all* fiber reinforced/resin matrix composites. There is some evidence [7] that such may be the case, at least for what has been referred to as "fiber or filament-dominated" laminates [12] in glass/epoxy, boron/epoxy, and graphite/epoxy systems.

Third, although the rationale behind the failure criteria is more fully explained in Ref 7, it should be mentioned here that LEFM essentially uses the concept of the point stress criterion in order to avoid dealing with the infinite stress at the crack tip. In fact, it is easily shown that it is precisely for this reason that a classical stress concentration approach predicts no hole size effect on tensile strength whereas an LEFM approach does predict a crack size effect on tensile strength, in spite of the fact that the stress solution for both is derived from the identical elliptical hole problem.

Fourth, the wisdom of using laminated plate theory to predict the stress distribution ahead of a notch in a laminated composite plate may be questioned in view of the known problems caused by the free-edge effect [13], matrix crazing [14], and material nonlinearity [15]. There is, however, reason to believe [16, 17] that for many laminates, the perturbation of the predicted stresses will be confined to a region small in size compared to the characteristic lengths, d_0 and a_0. Ultimately, of course, judgement of the models will be based on a comparison with experimental data.

Before proceding to the experimental program, two important observations that result from the failure criteria will be discussed. The first concerns the statistical nature of composite laminate failure. Assume that the distribution of uniaxial failure strengths of an unnotched laminate can be represented by a two-parameter Weibull distribution such that

$$P(\sigma_0 > \sigma) = e^{-(\sigma/\beta_0)^\alpha} \tag{19}$$

where σ_0 is the uniaxial tensile strength and β_0 and α are the experimentally obtained location and shape parameters, respectively. Then the distribution of notched failure strengths can be predicted from the predicted ratio of notched to unnotched failure strengths, σ_N^∞/σ_0. In particular, for a circular hole in an isotropic laminate, Eq 19 combined with the strength ratio from the point stress criterion, Eq 5, results in the predicted notched strength distribution

$$P(\sigma_N > \sigma) = e^{\frac{1}{4}I(\sigma/\beta_{N1})^\alpha} \tag{20}$$

where

$$\beta_{N1} = 2\beta_0/(2 + \xi_1^2 + 3\xi_1^4) \tag{21}$$

Similarly, the strength ratio from the average stress criterion, Eq 6, leads to the predicted notched strength distribution

$$P(\sigma_N > \sigma) = e^{-(\sigma/\beta_{N2})^\alpha} \qquad (22)$$

where

$$\beta_{N2} = 2\beta_0(1 - \zeta_2)/(2 - \zeta_2^2 - \zeta_2^4) \qquad (23)$$

Note that each of the criteria imply that the shape factor of the *notched* strength distribution is identical to that of the unnotched strength distribution, while the location parameter changes by an amount dependent on the hole size. Approximately identical shape factors for notched and unnotched failure strength distributions have been observed, for example, in Ref *18*, for the case of 0.1-in.-diameter circular holes in quasi-isotropic boron/epoxy laminates. It is of interest to compare the notched strength location parameter determined experimentally in Ref *18*, β_N = 47.25 ksi (the unnotched strength location parameter was determined to be β_0 = 60.92 ksi), with the values predicted using Eqs 21 and 23. These are, respectively, β_{N1} = 46.96 ksi and β_{N2} = 47.26 ksi, where the values of the characteristic lengths were chosen as d_0 = 0.04 in. and a_0 = 0.15 in. These particular values of d_0 and a_0 were chosen in Ref *7* to provide the best fit for data from holes in quasi-isotropic glass/epoxy and center cracks in $(0/\pm 45)_s$ graphite/epoxy. Note the excellent agreement of the predictions with the experimentally determined values.

The second observation concerns the use of an Irwin type correction factor in conjunction with Eqs 11 and 13 to produce a more constant value of the critical stress intensity factor for all crack lengths. In particular, consider the modified critical stress intensity factor, K_Q', defined in the following manner

$$K_Q' = \sigma_N^\infty \sqrt{\pi(c + c_0)} \qquad (24)$$

where $c + c_0$ is an effective half crack length with c_0 being an adjustment used to operationally induce a more constant value of the stress intensity factor. This adjustment was first introduced by Irwin for homogeneous metals, as discussed in Ref *19*, and is equal to the plastic zone size which is estimated from the stress distribution in front of the crack tip and the yield strength of the metal. Since fiber-dominated laminates do not yield in the classical sense, such an adjustment in composite materials may represent a damage zone (distance over which matrix crazing and fiber breakage occurs) which is analogous to the plastic zone size in metals.

Equation 24 in conjunction with Eqs 11 and 13 yields

$$K_Q' = \sigma_0\sqrt{\pi(c + c_0)(1 - \zeta_3^2)} \tag{25}$$

$$K_Q' = \sigma_0\sqrt{\pi(c + c_0)(1 - \zeta_4)/(1 + \zeta_4)} \tag{26}$$

respectively. In an attempt to make K_Q' relatively independent of crack length, c_0 is chosen such that K_Q' approaches the asymptotic limit of K_Q as the implanted crack length, c, vanishes, that is, as $c \to 0$, $K_Q' \to \sigma_0\sqrt{2\pi d_0}$ for the point stress criterion and $K_Q' \to \sigma_0\sqrt{\pi a_0/2}$ for the average stress criterion. Application of these procedures to Eqs 25 and 26, respectively, yields

$$c_0 = 2d_0 \tag{27}$$

$$c_0 = a_0/2 \tag{28}$$

Equations 25 and 26 now become

$$K_Q' = \sigma_0\sqrt{\pi(c + 2d_0)(1 - \zeta_3^2)} \tag{29}$$

$$K_Q' = \sigma_0\sqrt{\pi a_0/2} \tag{30}$$

Thus, the average stress criterion yields a constant value of K_Q'. Although Eq 29 shows K_Q' is not independent of crack length for the point stress criterion, numerical calculations reveal a relatively constant value; for example, $d_0 = 0.04$ in. yields less than a 6 percent variation in K_Q' for all values of crack length.

It should be noted that Eq 24 implies the existence of an effective inherent flaw, that is, as $c \to 0$, $K_Q' \to \sigma_0\sqrt{\pi c_0}$. Since c_0 is related to d_0 and a_0, it is anticipated that these characteristic lengths will be influenced by the quality of the composite, that is, the inherent flaw size, c_0, will be larger for poor quality material, resulting in larger values of d_0 and a_0. Some evidence of such a trend can be found in Ref 18 where statistical data were presented on quasi-isotropic graphite/epoxy specimens containing a 0.277-in.-diameter hole. For this case $\beta_N = 39.2$ ksi (43.1 ksi when adjusted for the 1-in. finite width) and $\beta_0 = 49.4$ ksi. This material would appear to be of poor quality as β_0 is low compared to other data presented for similar type quasi-isotropic graphite/epoxy laminates. While the shape parameters were almost identical for notched and unnotched tensile strengths ($\alpha = 11.4$ for unnotched specimens and 11.5 for notched specimens), the low values again suggest a material of only marginal quality. The boron/epoxy data in Ref *18* yielded $\alpha = 20.72$ for notched specimens and $\alpha = 19.78$ for unnotched specimens. Using $d_0 = 0.15$ in. and $a_0 = 0.6$ in. in conjunction with Eqs 21 and 23 yields $\beta_{N1} = 41.3$ ksi and $\beta_{N2} = 40.9$ ksi, respectively. Both values of characteristic length imply an effective inherent flaw size of 0.3 in., while values of $c_0 = 0.08$ in. were obtained for all of the data in Ref *7* and for the boron/epoxy data in Ref *18*. Thus, we have some evidence that d_0 and a_0 may depend on α.

Experimental Program

The experimental program was designed to provide additional data for use in further evaluating the proposed uniaxial failure criteria. In particular, it was desired to determine whether the same values of the characteristic lengths, d_0 and a_0, found to provide the best predictions for the limited data in Ref *7*, could be used to predict failure in the case of other notch shapes, laminates, and material systems. In addition, it was desired to determine whether either the point stress or average stress criterion would result in consistantly better predictions. Thus, a program was completed that examined the effects of the material system, the lamination, and the stress gradient (notch shape and size) on the model predictions.

Specifically, two material systems were investigated: Scotchply 1002 and Thornel 300/Narmco 5208 supplied in prepreg by 3M Company and Whittaker Corporation, respectively. Two laminations of each material were used, namely, $(0/\pm 45/90)_{2s}$ and $(0/90)_{4s}$, so that all laminates were 16 plies thick. These particular laminates were chosen to span the range of structurally applicable laminates possessing essentially linear (or bilinear) uniaxial tensile behavior. $(\pm 45)_s$ laminates, which are currently of importance because of their use in crack arrestment strips, were not considered in the present program because of their nonlinear uniaxial tensile behavior. In addition, the $(0/90)_{4s}$ laminate provided a good test case because of its large stress concentration factor for a circular hole, namely, for T300/5208, $K_T^\infty = 5.11$.

The effect of notch shape and size were examined by considering both circular holes and sharp-tipped center cracks of sizes 0.1, 0.3, 0.6, and 1.0 in. (hole diameter or crack length). These combinations were considered to be a good test of the effect of the degree of stress concentration, since they represent the range from extremely narrow to extremely broad regions of concentration. The particular sizes chosen were made because previous data [*1, 7, 8*] have shown that the transition from unnotched behavior to large-notch size behavior occurs in this range of notch size.

In all, 116 tests were run, as shown in Tables 1 thru 3. Each data point represents the average of three ostensibly identical tests. This number of replicate tests was considered to be the absolute minimum number necessary

TABLE 1—*Circular holes.*

Specimen No.	Material	Laminate	L (in.)	W (in.)	t (in.)	$2R$ (in.)	σ_N (ksi)	$\sigma_N^{\infty\,b}$ (ksi)	$\sigma_N^{\infty}/\sigma_0$	Variation (%)
SH101-1, 2, 3	glass	$(0/\pm45/90)_{2S}$	5	0.996	0.137	0.100	32.3	32.7	0.70	+7.1 / −5.7
SH103-1, 2, 3	glass	$(0/\pm45/90)_{2S}$	5	0.998	1.141	0.297	23.7	26.4	0.57	+3.5 / −3.5
SH106-1, 2, 3	glass	$(0/\pm45/90)_{2S}$	10	1.994	0.142	0.596	20.4	22.7	0.49	+4.1 / −2.0
SH110-1, 2, 3	glass	$(0/\pm45/90)_{2S}$	15	2.992	0.154	0.997	17.4	20.0	0.43	+2.3 / −2.3
SHX01-1, 2, 3	glass	$(0/90)_{4S}$	5	0.996	0.137	0.101	42.3	42.8	0.70	+7.1 / −5.7
SHX03-1, 2, 3[a]	glass	$(0/90)_{4S}$	5	0.995	0.141	0.303	29.8	33.4	0.55	+1.8 / −3.6
SHX06-1, 2, 3	glass	$(0/90)_{4S}$	10	1.991	0.141	0.595	24.1	26.9	0.44	+4.5 / −2.3
SHX10-1, 2, 3	glass	$(0/90)_{4S}$	15	2.978	0.155	1.003	19.8	22.8	0.37	+2.7 / −2.7
GH101-1, 2, 3	graphite	$(0/\pm45/90)_{2S}$	5	0.994	0.080	0.103	51.1	51.7	0.72	+3.9 / −5.7
GH103-1, 2, 3	graphite	$(0/\pm45/90)_{2S}$	5	1.000	0.083	0.301	37.7	42.1	0.58	+10.3 / −13.8
GH106-1, 2, 3	graphite	$(0/\pm45/90)_{2S}$	10	1.998	0.082	0.603	34.9	39.0	0.54	+5.6 / −1.9
GH110-1, 2, 3	graphite	$(0/\pm45/90)_{2S}$	15	2.997	0.083	1.003	28.2	32.4	0.45	+4.4 / −4.4
GHX01-1, 2, 3	graphite	$(0/90)_{4S}$	5	0.990	0.089	0.102	70.5	71.3	0.77	+1.3 / −1.3
GHX03-1, 2, 3	graphite	$(0/90)_{4S}$	5	0.987	0.085	0.300	48.1	53.8	0.58	+5.2 / −3.4
GHX06-1, 2, 3	graphite	$(0/90)_{4S}$	10	1.990	0.090	0.596	41.6	46.4	0.50	+2.0 / −2.0
GHX10-1, 2, 3	graphite	$(0/90)_{4S}$	15	2.994	0.084	1.009	45.7	52.6	0.57	+3.5 / −8.8

[a] Average of two specimens, third was machined incorrectly.
[b] $\sigma_N^{\infty} = (K_T/K_T^{\infty})\,\sigma_{N\,\text{isotropic}}$

TABLE 2—*Center cracks.*

Specimen No.	Material	Laminate	L (in.)	W (in.)	t (in.)	$2c$ (in.)	σ_N (ksi)	$\sigma_N^{\infty b}$ (ksi)	$\sigma_N^{\infty}/\sigma_0$	Variation, (%)	K_Q^c (ksi$\sqrt{\text{in.}}$)
SCI01-1, 2, 3[a]	glass	$(0/\pm45/90)_{2S}$	5	0.984	0.141	0.114	32.8	32.9	0.71	+5.6 / −7.0	13.8
SC103-1, 2, 3	glass	$(0/\pm45/90)_{2S}$	5	0.991	0.137	0.304	25.2	26.8	0.58	+6.9 / −8.6	18.5
SC106-1, 2, 3	glass	$(0/\pm45/90)_{2S}$	10	1.991	0.147	0.580	20.4	21.5	0.47	+0.0 / −2.1	20.6
SC110-1, 2, 3	glass	$(0/\pm45/90)_{2S}$	15	2.994	0.157	0.976	15.7	16.8	0.36	+2.8 / −0.0	20.8
SCX01-1, 2, 3	glass	$(0/90)_{4S}$	5	0.991	0.139	0.103	39.9	39.9	0.65	+6.2 / −4.6	16.0
SCX03-1, 2, 3	glass	$(0/90)_{4S}$	5	0.984	0.136	0.285	29.6	31.2	0.51	+5.9 / −7.8	20.9
SCX06-1, 2, 3	glass	$(0/90)_{4S}$	10	1.990	0.144	0.585	24.7	26.1	0.43	+4.7 / −7.0	25.0
SCX10-1, 2, 3	glass	$(0/90)_{4S}$	15	2.993	0.156	1.018	16.9	18.3	0.30	+6.7 / −13.3	23.2
GCI01-1, 2, 3	graphite	$(0/\pm45/90)_{2S}$	5	0.996	0.081	0.109	62.9	63.0	0.88	+9.1 / −5.7	26.1
GCI03-1, 2, 3	graphite	$(0/\pm45/90)_{2S}$	5	1.001	0.081	0.307	46.0	48.9	0.69	+7.2 / −10.1	34.0
GCI06-1, 2, 3	graphite	$(0/\pm45/90)_{2S}$	10	1.994	0.083	0.599	41.7	44.2	0.62	+1.6 / −3.2	42.9
GCI10-1, 2, 3	graphite	$(0/\pm45/90)_{2S}$	15	3.000	0.082	0.990	34.7	37.3	0.52	+1.9 / −0.0	46.5
GCX01-1, 2, 3	graphite	$(0/90)_{4S}$	5	0.988	0.086	0.109	68.7	68.8	0.75	+9.3 / −6.7	28.5
GCX03-1, 2, 3	graphite	$(0/90)_{4S}$	5	0.986	0.084	0.304	46.7	49.7	0.54	+7.4 / −11.1	34.2
GCX06-1, 2, 3	graphite	$(0/90)_{4S}$	10	1.987	0.086	0.599	46.9	49.8	0.54	+18.5 / −24.1	48.2
GCX10-1, 2, 3	graphite	$(0/90)_{4S}$	15	2.992	0.085	0.995	46.4	50.0	0.54	+5.6 / −9.3	62.4

[a] Average of two specimens, third was machined incorrectly.
[b] $\sigma_{0N}^{\infty} = (K_I/K_I^{\infty})_{\text{isotropic}} \sigma_N$.
[c] $K_Q = \sigma_N^{\infty}\sqrt{\pi c}$.

TABLE 3—*Tension coupons.*

Specimen No.	Material	Laminate	L (in.)	W (in.)	t (in.)	σ_0 (ksi)	Variation (%)
STI-1, 2, 3, 4, 5	glass	$(0/\pm45/90)_{2S}$	4.5	0.743	0.145	46.4	+15.7 −12.3
STX-1, 2, 3, 4, 5	glass	$(0/90)_{4S}$	4.5	0.746	0.145	61.3	+18.9 −14.4
GTI-1, 2, 3, 4, 5	graphite	$(0/\pm45/90)_{2S}$	4.5	0.746	0.082	71.7	+4.0 −3.1
GTX-1, 2, 3, 4, 5	graphite	$(0/90)_{4S}$	4.5	0.737	0.085	92.4	+10.9 −14.1

to produce meaningful results due to the statistical nature of composite failure. As will be discussed later, even this number may have been too few to make absolute conclusions possible.

For each laminate of each material system, two plates were laid up and cured in an autoclave using the prepreg supplier's recommended curing procedure. Two plates were necessary because of autoclave size limitations. Fiber volume fractions were determined to be approximately 66 percent for all plates of the T300/5208 material system. From one plate all of the specimens containing both the 1.0 in. holes and cracks were cut while the other plate supplied all the specimens containing the smaller sized holes and cracks. In addition, three tension coupons were taken from the center of the large specimen plate and two were taken from the center of the smaller specimen plate.

Each notched specimen was essentially a straight-sided tension specimen (see Fig. 3) with either a centrally located drilled hole of the proper size or a central crack formed by drilling a 0.01-in.-diameter pilot hole and then using a 0.005-in.-diameter diamond wire to complete the crack. All of the circular-hole specimens suffered some degree of delamination near the hole on the back side of the specimen where the drill exited, while the center cracks all exhibited some degree of deviation from a straight line due to wandering of the diamond wire. The dimensions of the various specimens are given in Tables 1 thru 3, where averages of three specimens are shown. It should be observed that no attempt was made to make all the specimens geometrically similar. In particular, although the gage length (length between tabs) of all specimens was five times the width, the hole diameter or crack width to specimen width ratio was nominally 0.1, 0.3, 0.3, and 0.33 for the 0.1, 0.3, 0.6, and 1.0-in. notch sizes, respectively. This was done purposely since, as long as the normal stress distribution ahead of the notch is known, the notch width to specimen width ratio should have no effect on the model's predictions.

All specimens were ramp loaded to failure at a rate of 20 lb/s in a closed-loop MTS machine to avoid any dynamic loading effects. Although acoustic emission was recorded for all specimens and many were extensively strain gaged, only the load to failure is reported in the present paper. The other data were gathered for future analysis.

Data Reduction

From the failure load of each unnotched tension coupon, the failure stress, σ_0, was computed. Similarly, the gross failure stress, σ_N, of the notched specimens was obtained from the failure load of these specimens. These values were then adjusted for all laminates by multiplying σ_N by the isotropic finite width correction factor, K_T/K_T^∞ or K_1/K_1^∞ for holes and cracks, respectively, to obtain the notched, infinite width plate failure

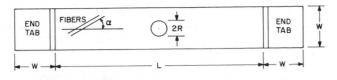

CIRCULAR HOLE SPECIMENS

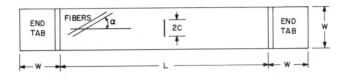

CENTER CRACKED SPECIMENS

FIG. 3—*Geometry of circular hole and center cracked test specimens.*

stress, σ_N^∞. Approximate expressions for these factors can be found in Refs *20* and *21,* respectively, and are given by the relationships

$$K_T / K_T^\infty = \frac{2 + (1 - 2R/W)^3}{3(1 - 2R/W)} \tag{31}$$

$$K_1 / K_1^\infty = \sqrt{(W/\pi c) \tan(\pi c/W)} \tag{32}$$

where W is the finite specimen width. Equation 31 is very accurate for $2R/W \leqslant 1/2$, while Eq 32 is highly accurate in the range $2c/W \leqslant 1/3$. Finally, the notched, infinite width failure stress for each notched specimen was normalized by dividing by the average (of five specimens) unnotched tensile strength, that is, the ratio $\sigma_N^\infty / \sigma_0$ was formed. The averages of three test specimens are shown in Tables 1 and 2 along with the variations from the averages. In addition, the average fracture toughness, K_Q, for each of the center-cracked geometries is listed in Table 2.

The predicted values of $\sigma_N^\infty / \sigma_0$ and K_Q were determined from Eqs 5, 8, 11, and 13, and Eqs 15 and 16, respectively. The infinite plate stress concentration factor, K_T^∞, was computed to be $K_T^\infty = 3.74$ for the $(0/90)_{4S}$ Scotchply plate and $K_T^\infty = 5.11$ for the $(0/90)_{4S}$ T300/5208 plate, where in each case the necessary stiffnesses were computed using laminated plate theory and the material properties given in Table 4. The values used for the characteristic lengths were $d_0 = 0.04$ in. and $a_0 = 0.15$ in. *It is important to note that the choice of d_0 and a_0 indicated is exactly the values of d_0 and a_0 used in Ref 7.* That is the values of the characteristic lengths used here are *not* chosen from a best fit of the present data but from a best fit of data from holes in quasi-isotropic Scotchply 1002 and cracks in $(0/\pm45)$ T300/5208.

TABLE 4—*Material properties.*

Material	Elastic Constants
Thornel 300/Narmco 5208	$E_{11} = 21.4 \times 10^3$ ksi $E_{12} = 1.6 \times 10^3$ ksi $G_{12} = 0.77 \times 10^3$ ksi $\nu_{12} = 0.29$
Scotchply 1002	$E_{11} = 5.6 \times 10^3$ ksi $E_{22} = 1.2 \times 10^3$ ksi $G_{12} = 0.6 \times 10^3$ ksi $\nu_{12} = 0.26$

Before comparing the experimental and predicted results, a comment is in order concerning an assumption made in the data reduction. The original failure criteria, Eqs 4 and 7, should be based upon the theoretical normal stress distribution ahead of the notch in the finite width plate. In essence, the method of data reduction used in this study assumes that the finite width stress distribution is equal to the stress distribution in an infinite plate multiplied by the isotropic finite width correction factor. Although it has been shown in Ref *22,* for example, that isotropic finite width correction factors can be applied to anisotropic plates containing center cracks to obtain stress intensity factors, that this is also true for circular holes has not been shown conclusively [2], nor has any comparison of the stress distributions been made for either cracks or holes. Thus, a standard constant finite element program was used to generate the normal stress ahead of a hole and a crack in a finite width specimen of hole diameter or crack length to width ratio of one third for all four of the material systems and laminates used in the present program. These results were plotted against the normal stress distribution obtained by multiplying the infinite plate stress [9] by the isotropic finite width correction factors. A typical result is shown in Fig. 4 for the case of a hole in a (0/90) T300/5208 plate where it is seen that the comparison is quite good. Thus, it was concluded that the amount of error introduced through the assumption was negligible for our study. For larger hole diameter to width ratios, this assumption would have to be reevaluated and the actual finite width distribution used if necessary, especially since the basic character of the stress distribution in isotropic materials becomes increasingly linear for $2R/W > 1/2$ [23, 24].

Results

First, it is interesting to examine some typical failed specimens, both notched and unnotched, for each of the materials and laminations used, as shown in Figs. 5 thru 8. The similarity between the failure surfaces of the notched (both holes and cracks) and unnotched specimens is quite

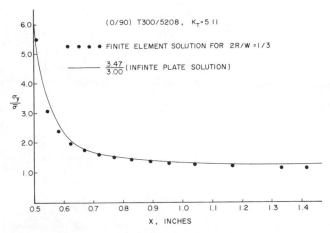

FIG. 4—*Comparison of normal stress distributions across the ligament of an anisotropic finite width plate containing a circular hole.*

FIG. 5—*Failed (0/ ±45/90)$_{2S}$ Scotchply 1002 specimens (notched and unnotched).*

evident. No single through-crack propagation mode of failure is observed in the photos, nor was any observed during testing *before* ultimate failure occurred. In fact, prior to final failure, no damage of any sort visible to the unaided eye was seen in any of the T300/5208 specimens. In contrast, near the ultimate failure load, zones of crazed material did form in the Scotchply specimens in regions of high stress concentrations near the notches. Through cracks, however, did not form.

Graphical comparison of the experimentally obtained failure stresses with the predicted values is shown in Figs. 9 thru 16, where σ_N/σ_0 is plotted

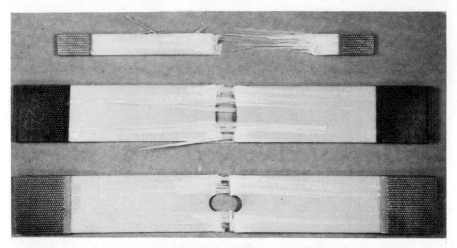

FIG. 6—*Failed (0/90)₄ₛ Scotchply 1002 specimens (notched and unnotched).*

FIG. 7—*Failed (0/±45/90)₂ₛ T300/5208 specimens (notched and unnotched).*

versus notch size. In addition, in Figs. 17 thru 20, comparison is made of the experimentally obtained fracture toughness, K_Q, to the predicted values for various length cracks. In all figures, the solid dots represent the average experimental value (of three tests), the vertical line through the dots represents the data spread and the solid and dashed curves represent the predicted values using the average and point stress failure criterion, respectively.

For the holes in the $(0/\pm45/90)_{2S}$ and $(0/90)_{4S}$ Scotchply 1002 and the holes in the $(0/\pm45/90)_{2S}$ T300/5208, Figs. 9 thru 11, the comparison between the experimental and predicted failure stress is quite good, with

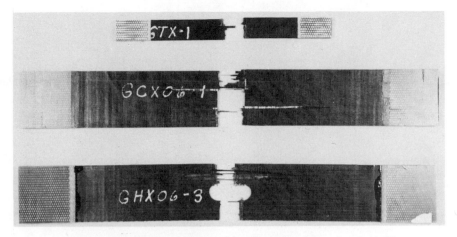

FIG. 8—*Failed (0/90)₄ₛ T300/5208 specimens (notched and unnotched).*

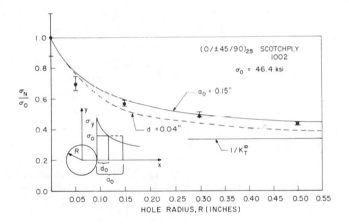

FIG. 9—*Comparison of predicted and experimental failure stresses for circular holes in (0/ ± 45/90)₂ₛ Scotchply 1002.*

neither the point stress nor the average stress criterion giving consistently better results. For the holes in the (0/90)₄ₛ T300/5208, Fig. 12, the comparison is quite good with the single exception of the largest, 1.0-in. diameter, hole where the error is roughly 35 percent for the average stress criterion. Inspection of Table 1 reveals that a peculiar situation exists for this point in that the gross failure stress, σ_N, was greater than for the smaller 0.6-in.-diameter hole size, contrary to normal expectations. Part of the explanation for the divergence of this point from the predicted value can be made by recalling that the plate used for the large hole size was different than for

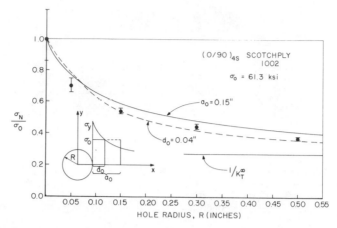

FIG. 10—*Comparison of predicted and experimental failure stresses for circular holes in (0/90)₄ₛ Scotchply 1002.*

the three smaller hole sizes. Thus, a possiblility exists that the two plates were of different strengths. In fact, two tension coupons were cut from the failed specimen containing the 1.0-in.-diameter hole, one from either side of the hole, and tested. The average strength of these two unnotched specimens was 106.9 ksi compared to the average strength used of 92.4 ksi. Using this value for the unnotched strength of the laminate results in the open circle shown in Fig. 12 which is closer to the predicted curve, although still considerably in error.

For the cracks in the $(0/\pm45/90)_{2S}$ and $(0/90)_{4S}$ Scotchply 1002, Figs. 13 and 14 or 17 and 18, the comparison of predicted and experimental strengths is reasonably good. For the $(0/\pm45/90)_{2S}$ T300/5208, however, the results are rather poor, that is, roughly a 27 percent error for the point stress

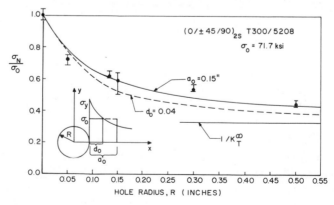

FIG. 11—*Comparison of predicted and experimental failure stresses for circular holes in $(0/\pm45/90)_{2S}$ T300/5208.*

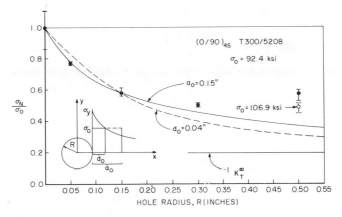

FIG. 12—*Comparison of predicted and experimental failure stresses for circular holes in (0/90)$_{4S}$ T300/5208.*

criterion applied to the 1.0-in.-diameter hole. At this time, no explanation of the discrepancy is available. However, the experimentally obtained value of fracture toughness, $K_Q = 46.5$ ksi$\sqrt{\text{in.}}$, seems high for quasi-isotropic T300/5208. For cracks in the (0/90)$_{4S}$ T300/5208, the experimental, predicted comparison is quite good for the two smaller crack sizes, but rather poor for the two larger crack sizes. The poor comparison for the 0.6-in.-length crack can be explained by virtue of the abnormally large data scatter for this point. Part of the explanation for the poor comparison for the 1.0-in.-length crack can again be made on the basis of two postmortem tension coupons cut from the notched specimen. These had an average unnotched strength of 103.1 ksi. Using this value for the un-

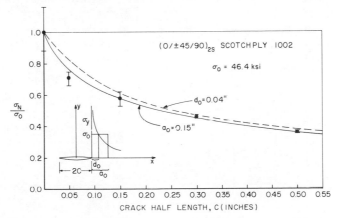

FIG. 13—*Comparison of predicted and experimental failure stresses for center cracks in (0/±45/90)$_{2S}$ Scotchply 1002.*

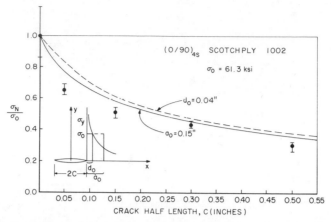

FIG. 14—*Comparison of predicted and experimental failure stresses for center cracks in* (0/90)*$_{4S}$ Scotchply 1002.*

notched strength of the material lowers the data point as shown by the open dots in Figs. 16 and 20.

Discussion and Conclusions

Two models have been proposed to qualitatively explain the hole size effect [1] without the use of linear elastic fracture mechanics concepts. It was shown that this phenomenon is explainable in a very simple and straightforward way by simply considering the stress distribution ahead of a notch. In addition, the use of the models as a design tool for predicting the ultimate uniaxial failure load of notched composites has been evaluated through comparison with the results of an experimental program.

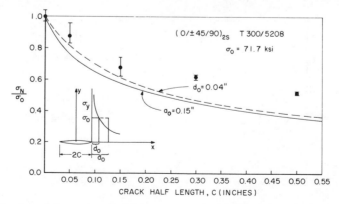

FIG. 15—*Comparison of predicted and experimental failure stresses for center cracks in* (0/±45/90)*$_{2S}$ T300/5208.*

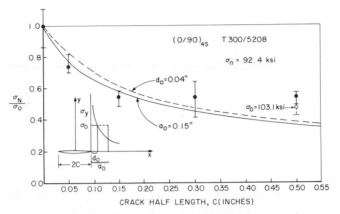

FIG. 16—*Comparison of predicted and experimental failure stresses for center cracks in* $(0/90)_{4S}$ *T300/5208.*

In spite of the large number of tests completed, it is felt that no conclusive statement about the accuracy of the models can be made at this time, due to the large scatter obtained in the data. The scatter appears to be largely due to two factors: (1) the cure cycle used was the same for all plates of the same material system, thereby failing to account for differences in the prepreg material used, resulting in considerable strength differences from plate to plate and, apparently, even within each plate; and (2) the machining of the notches which resulted in rough holes and wandering cracks. It is felt that a definite conclusion regarding the constancy of the characteristic lengths for various laminates of glass/epoxy, boron/epoxy, and graphite/epoxy must await more data resulting from a carefully done program which takes the statistical nature of the failure into account.

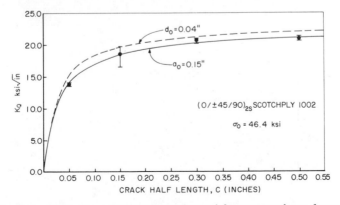

FIG. 17—*Comparison of predicted and experimental fracture toughness for center cracks in* $(0/\pm45/90)_{2S}$ *Scotchply 1002.*

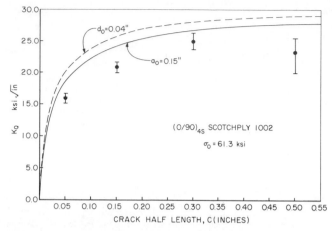

FIG. 18—*Comparison of predicted and experimental fracture toughness for center cracks in (0/90)$_{4S}$ Scotchply 1002.*

Combined with the data of Ref 7, however, the data of the present program seem to indicate the usefulness of the present models as design tools.

Finally, it should be noted that, for the present, certain limitations are inherent in the use of the models. Thus, in its present form, the failure criteria can be expected to make adequate predictions of failure of notched laminates under *uniaxial* loading conditions only. Also, until tests can be run on laminates which exhibit substantial nonlinear behavior under uniaxial tension, such as (± 45)$_S$ laminates, use of the criteria should be restricted to what have been called fiber dominated laminates, that is, laminates exhibiting essentially linear (or bilinear) uniaxial stress-strain curves.

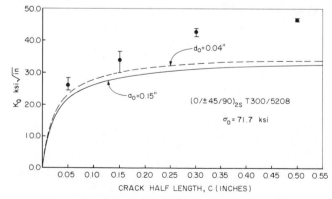

FIG. 19—*Comparison of predicted and experimental fracture toughness for center cracks in (0/$\pm$45/90)$_{2S}$ T300/5208.*

Acknowledgments

One of the authors (R. J. Nuismer) wishes to acknowledge the support of the National Research Council through the Resident Research Associate Program. This work is part of a continuing in-house research program sponsored by the Mechanics and Surface Interactions Branch of the Nonmetallic Materials Division, Air Force Materials Laboratory. The authors wish to acknowledge R. Kim, J. Camping, T. Richardson, and C. Lovett of the University of Dayton Research Institute for the fabrication, preparation, and testing of composite experimental specimens.

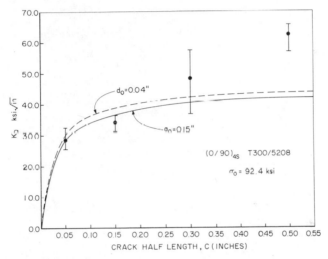

FIG. 20—*Comparison of predicted and experimental fracture toughness for center cracks in (0/90)$_{4S}$ T300/5208.*

References

[1] Waddoups, M. E., Eisenmann, J. R., and Kaminski, B. E., *Journal of Composite Materials,* Vol. 5, 1971, pp. 446–454.
[2] Whiteside, J. B., Daniel, I. M., and Rowlands, R. E., "The Behavior of Advanced Filamentary Composite Plates with Cutouts," Air Force Flight Dynamics Laboratory Technical Report AFFDL-TR-73-48, June 1973.
[3] Zweben, C., *Engineering Fracture Mechanics,* Vol. 6, 1974, pp. 1–10.
[4] Cruse, T. A., *Journal of Composite Materials,* Vol. 7, 1973, pp. 218–229.
[5] Bowie, O. L., *Journal of Mathematics and Physics,* Vol. 35, 1956, pp. 60–71.
[6] Nuismer, R. J. and Hahn, H. T., presented at the American Society for Testing and Materials, "Composite Reliability Conference," Las Vegas, Nev., 15–16 April 1974.
[7] Whitney, J. M. and Nuismer, R. J., *Journal of Composite Materials,* Vol. 8, 1974, pp. 253–265.
[8] Konish, H. J., Jr. and Cruse, T. A. in *Composite Reliability, ASTM STP 580,* American Society for Testing and Materials, 1975.

[9] Lekhnitskii, S. G., *Anisotropic Plates,* translated from the Second Russian Edition by S. W. Tsai and T. Cheron, Gordan and Breach, Science Publishers, Inc., New York, 1968.

[10] Ashton, J. E. and Whitney, J. M., *Theory of Laminated Plates,* Technomic Publishing Co., Stamford, Conn., 1970.

[11] Konish, H. J., Jr. and Whitney, J. M., submitted to AIAA/ASME/SAE 16th Structures, Structural Dynamics, and Materials Conference.

[12] Halpin, J. C., Jerina, K. L., and Johnson, T. A., in *Analysis of the Test Methods for High Modulus Fibers and Composites, ASTM STP 521,* American Society for Testing and Materials, 1973, pp. 5–64.

[13] Pagano, N. J. and Pipes, R. B., *Journal of Composite Materials,* Vol. 5, 1971, pp. 50–57.

[14] Mandell, J. F., Wang, S. S., and McGarry, F. J., "Fracture of Graphite Fiber Reinforced Composites," Air Force Materials Laboratory Technical Report AFML-TR-73-142, 1973.

[15] Hahn, H. T., *Journal of Composite Materials,* Vol. 7, 1973, pp. 257–271.

[16] Konish, H. J., Jr., Swedlow, J. L., and Cruse, T. A., *Journal of Composite Materials,* Vol. 6, 1972, pp. 114–124.

[17] Wang, S. S., Mandell, J. F., and McGarry, F. J. in this symposium.

[18] Waddoups, M. E. and Halpin, J. C., *Computers and Structures,* Vol. 4, May 1974.

[19] McClintock, F. A. and Irwin, G. R., *Fracture Toughness Testing and Its Applications, ASTM STP 381,* American Society for Testing and Materials, 1965, pp. 84–113.

[20] Peterson, R. E., *Stress Concentration Factors,* Wiley, New York, 1974, pp. 110–111.

[21] Paris, P. C. and Sih, G. C., *Fracture Toughness Testing and Its Applications, ASTM STP 381,* American Society for Testing and Materials, 1965, pp. 84–113.

[22] Synder, M. D. and Cruse, T. A., "Crack Tip Stress Intensity Factors In Finite Anisotropic Plates," Air Force Materials Laboratory Report AFML-TR-73-209, Aug. 1973.

[23] Coker, E. G. and Filon, L. N. G., *A Treatise on Photo-Elasticity,* revised by H. T. Jessop, Cambridge University Press, 1957, pp. 481–489.

[24] Belie, R. G. and Appl, F. J., *Experimental Mechanics,* Vol. 12, 1972, pp. 190–195: "Discussion," Vol. 13, 1973, pp. 255–256.

J. M. Slepetz[1] and L. Carlson[1]

Fracture of Composite Compact Tension Specimens

REFERENCE: Slepetz, J. M. and Carlson, L., **"Fracture of Composite Compact Tension Specimens,"** *Fracture Mechanics of Composites, ASTM STP 593,* American Society for Testing and Materials, 1975, pp. 143–162.

ABSTRACT: Fracture experiments were carried out on compact tension specimens of unidirectional and cross-ply S-glass/epoxy and graphite/epoxy. Fracture toughness values were determined by the compliance calibration technique and by measuring the area under the load-displacement curve. In unidirectional specimens, crack extension was always parallel to the fibers and was dependent on crack length. Toughness did not vary significantly with fiber orientation relative to the load direction in unidirectional S-glass/epoxy. Tests on cross-ply S-glass specimens were not valid because crack propagation did not occur; instead, a zone containing a system of superficial parallel cracks and other damage developed, which extended with increasing load. Cross-ply graphite specimens, on the other hand, did appear to give valid test results although the cracks propagated were not always straight and other damage mechanisms were also present. Toughness values for cross-ply graphite were approximately two orders of magnitude higher than for unidirectional specimens due chiefly to the fracture resistance of fibers transverse to the crack. Toughness values determined by the compliance calibration method were consistent with reported values obtained by other methods.

KEY WORDS: fracture properties, composite materials, fractures (materials), crack propagation, mechanical properties, fiber composites, evaluation, tests

The prediction of failure in fiber reinforced composites having geometric discontinuities or inherent material defects is perplexing due to the complex fracture mechanisms which are characteristic of heterogeneous materials. Linear elastic fracture mechanics has been applied to failure phenomena in composites with some success [1–5][2] despite the difference in behavior from homogeneous materials. The use of fracture mechanics to predict failure is based on the existence of a material property, fracture toughness, defined by either the critical stress intensity factor, K_c, or critical strain energy release rate, G_c. These two properties are equivalent,

---

[1] Civil engineer and research assistant, respectively, Army Materials and Mechanics Research Center, Watertown, Mass. 02172.

[2] The italic numbers in brackets refer to the list of references appended to this paper.

being related through the elastic constants of the material [6]. The relationship between stress intensity factor, K, and strain energy release rate, G, for an orthotropic material in the crack opening mode is

$$G = K^2 \left(\frac{A_{11}A_{22}}{2}\right)^{1/2} \left[\frac{A_{22}}{A_{11}} + \frac{2A_{12} + A_{66}}{2A_{11}}\right]^{1/2} \tag{1}$$

A_{11}, A_{12}, etc. are the elastic compliances associated with the principal material directions. G_c is defined as the value of G at which unstable crack growth occurs.

G can be determined experimentally by compliance calibration of compact tension specimens. The relatively high load point displacements obtained with this type of specimen make it well suited to the compliance calibration technique. Also, under fixed grip conditions, crack growth is inherently stable in the compact tension specimen. Because G decreases with crack length, a crack which propagates at an instability load is generally arrested after a short growth interval. Consequently, a number of toughness measurements can be made on a single specimen [7]. The dependence of toughness on crack length and the development of various fracture mechanisms can be studied more closely since the failure process is controlled.

Most of the work in fracture of composites has been conducted on specimens other than the compact tension type. The applicability of linear elastic fracture mechanics to unidirectional composites in which the crack direction is predetermined to be parallel to the fibers was established in early studies by Wu [1,2] and extended by Lauraitis [3]. Wu developed an interaction relationship for combined Mode I and Mode II fracture using primarily center-notched tension specimens in the experiments. Lauraitis proposed a composite failure criterion based on the existence of inherent microcracks with the critical strain energy release rate, G_c, as the basic strength parameter. Unnotched tension specimens were used to verify the criterion. The extension of fracture mechanics to angle-ply and cross-ply materials has been less satisfactory because cracks do not always propagate in a direction of material symmetry as in unidirectional composites and because more complex damage phenomena such as delamination between plies and splitting within plies occur. Fracture of cross-ply composites has been studied using center or edge-notched tension specimens [4,5,8] and notched bend specimens [4,8]. The present study utilizes compact tension specimens to investigate fracture behavior in unidirectional and cross-ply composites. The main objectives are to identify the failure processes which occur in both types of laminates, determine the critical strain energy release rate, G_c, and evaluate the suitability of a fracture mechanics approach to cross-ply composites.

Experimental Procedures

Materials and Specimens

The compact tension specimens were machined from laminate panels of S-glass or graphite/epoxy which had been fabricated commercially by a tape lay-up and autoclave cure process. The S-glass panels were 1002S Scotchply,[3] 12 plies thick; and the graphite laminates were Modulite[4] 5208, eight plies thick. Both high modulus graphite (MOD I) and high strength graphite (MOD II) panels were tested. The laminates were fabricated with all unidirectional plies or with a balanced and symmetric cross-ply configuration having equal numbers of plies in two orthogonal directions. The elastic properties of test materials were determined by tension and shear tests on coupon specimens and are given in Table 1 along with the nominal volume fraction of fibers in the cured laminate.

TABLE 1—*Laminate properties.*

Material	E_1	E_2	G_{12}	μ_{12}	Fiber Volume, %
		lb/in.$^2 \times 10^6$			
1002 S-glass/epoxy					
Unidirectional	6.9	2.3	1.0	0.28	55
Crossply	4.7	4.7	1.1	0.14	
MOD I-5208 graphite/epoxy					
Unidirectional	19.9	1.11	0.93	0.32	40
Crossply	12.0	12.0	0.93	0.021	
MOD II-5208 graphite/epoxy					
Unidirectional	19.5	0.96	1.02	0.32	60
Crossply	12.1	12.1	0.95	0.035	

The compact tension specimen configuration used in most of the fracture experiments is shown in Fig. 1. In unidirectional S-glass/epoxy specimens the fiber direction with respect to the load direction was a test parameter, the various orientations being 0°, 30°, 45°, 60°, and 90°. Tests on unidirectional graphite specimens were conducted only with 0° or 90° fiber orientation. Cross-ply specimens of both S-glass and graphite were tested with the outer plies oriented at 0°, 45°, or 90° with respect to the applied load. It was necessary to constrain the cross-ply specimens to prevent out-of-plane bending. This was accomplished by clamping 0.125 in. thick lubricated steel plates to both sides of the specimen. The specimen in-plane compliance was unaffected, but out-of-plane deformation was satisfactorily limited. The test plan employed in the study is given in Table 2.

[3] Trade name, 3M Company.
[4] Trade name, Whittaker Division of NARMCO.

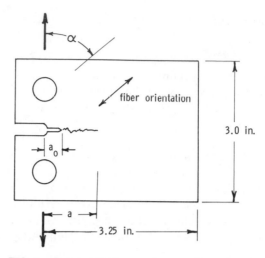

FIG. 1—*Compact tension specimen configuration.*

Compliance Test Procedure

Fracture toughness, characterized by the critical strain energy release rate, was determined using the compliance calibration technique. The compact tension specimens were loaded in an approximately fixed grip mode at a cross-head speed of 0.01 in./min. Load point displacement was measured by means of a clip gage. Displacement, together with applied load, were plotted on an *X-Y* recorder. The usual procedure followed was to load the specimen until an increment of crack propagated from the machined notch. Under the test grip conditions the load decreased sharply when this occurred and the crack was arrested. The new crack length was measured and the specimen was unloaded and reloaded to determine the change in compliance. The procedure was repeated a number of times until the crack had propagated to about 80 percent of the specimen width. A least squares curve fit was made to the experimental compliance calibration versus crack length relationship. The function found to best fit the compliance data over the widest range of crack lengths was

$$C = A_1(a/w) + A_2(a/w)^3 + A_3 \frac{2 + a/w}{(1 - a/w)^2} \tag{2}$$

in which C is compliance, a is crack length, and w is specimen width measured from the load line. A_1, A_2, and A_3 are the constants determined from the least squares fit. It can be seen that the three terms on the right side of Eq 2 qualitatively represent the compliance contributions due to beam shear, bending, and net section stress, respectively, in the compact tension specimen.

For an elastic body with an incrementally growing crack the strain energy release rate, G, can be determined experimentally from Ref 6.

$$G = \frac{F^2}{2t} \frac{dC}{da} \tag{3}$$

where F is the applied load, t is specimen thickness, and dC/da is the derivative of compliance with respect to crack length obtained from the experimental compliance curve, Eq 2. In this study, G_c was defined as the value G at which a crack in the specimen begins to grow unstably before being arrested. This occurs at a load, F_c, taken as the maximum load in the cycle of crack growth.

Fracture Work Procedure

In addition to the compliance technique the average fracture energy was determined by measuring the area under the load-displacement curve during an interval of crack extension. Under quasi-static loading conditions this method provided a rough check on the results obtained by compliance calibration; however, the latter is predicated on elastic behavior while the total fracture energy under the load curve would include any energy

TABLE 2—Test plan.

Laminate	α	No. of Tests	Initial Notch Length
1002 S-glass/epoxy			
Unidirectional	0	4	3/8
	90	12	3/8
	30	4	3/8
	45	4	3/8
	60	4	3/8
Crossply	0	4	3/4
	90	4	3/4
	45	2	3/4
MOD I graphite/epoxy			
Unidirectional	0	4	3/8
	90	4	3/8
Crossply	0	2	3/4
	9	2	3/4
	45	4	3/4
MOD II graphite/epoxy			
Unidirectional	0	4	3/8
	90	4	3/8
Crossply	0	8	3/4
	90	8	3/4
	45	4	3/4

dissipated by nonconservative behavior such as plastic deformation. An elastic finite element analysis of the compact tension specimen was undertaken to obtain an estimate of the variation of compliance with crack length. Plane stress orthotropic elements were used having the elastic properties given in Table 1 for the respective materials employed in the study. This was done to determine the suitability of using analytical rather than experimental calibration procedures as is commonly done with metal compact tension specimens.

Experimental Results

Unidirectional Specimens

Crack extension occurred parallel to the fibers in unidirectional compact tension specimens regardless of load orientation. This preferred crack orientation has previously been observed in other types of specimen [1,3,8] and causes some difficulty in data interpretation. Except for the case $\alpha = 90°$, crack growth along the fiber direction occurs by a combination of crack opening and forward shear fracture modes (Mode I and Mode II, respectively). The energy contributions of each mode are not experimentally separable by the compliance technique. Only when $\alpha = 90°$ would crack growth be expected to be by Mode I fracture only. In principle, the compliance technique is not limited to measuring G for Mode I fracture [6,9]; however, experimental difficulties in obtaining the compliance derivative of Eq 3 accurately for the inclined crack and specimen geometry employed make the application questionable. The work of fracture, W_f, measured by the area under the load-displacement curve also comprises the contributions of both modes. W_f was used instead of G_c to investigate the variation of fracture energy with fiber orientation in unidirectional S-glass specimens.

The load-displacement behavior of S-glass and graphite specimens was essentially linear until the onset of incremental crack growth. This is seen in Fig. 2 which shows the successive load displacement curves obtained for a unidirectional MOD II specimen with $\alpha = 90°$. For clarity the unloading curves are not shown. The compliance curves for MOD I and MOD II specimens appear in Fig. 3 with the finite-element values shown as the dashed line. The latter predictions are significantly higher than measured compliances except for small crack lengths. Crack growth in graphite specimens occurred typically by short pop-in bursts accompanied by a sharp decrease in load as seen in Fig. 2. With S-glass specimens, however, crack growth occurred by slow tearing, giving the load-deformation curve a rounded appearance at the top of the load cycle instead of the sharp peaks observed with graphite specimens. In addition to matrix

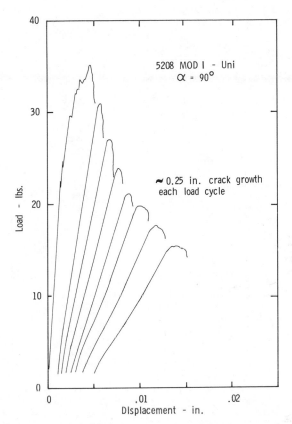

FIG. 2—*Load-displacement history for a unidirectional MOD I graphite/epoxy specimen.*

crack propagation all unidirectional specimens, but especially S-glass specimens, exhibited some degree of fiber bridging behind the advancing crack tip. This phenomenom is pictured in Fig. 4a which shows the network of fibers being pulled across the crack surface well behind the crack tip. In Fig. 4b these fibers are shown after the crack has completely penetrated the specimen. This fiber bridging action tends to increase both the specimen stiffness and toughness. The relative effect of this action was studied by machining away these fibers after each cycle of crack growth in tests on several S-glass specimens. The compliance curves obtained for natural and machined cracks are shown in Fig. 5 along with the finite element values represented by the dashed line. The compliance values for the machined notch (solid data points) were the highest observed; and the finite element predicted values were intermediate to those of the machined and natural crack values.

The fracture toughness, G_c, of S-glass specimens is shown as a function of normalized crack length in Fig. 6. The values obtained for specimens

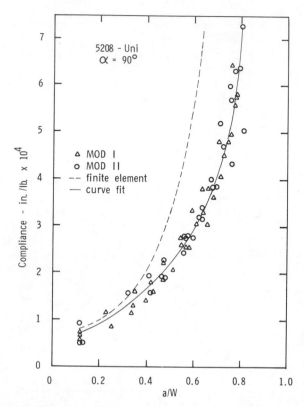

FIG. 3—*Compliance versus crack length curves for MOD I and MOD II specimens.*

with natural cracks showed a dependence on crack length up to about 30 percent of the specimen width, after which G_c leveled off at a mean value of 7.6 lb/in. The dependence on crack length can be attributed to the development of the fiber bridging action just discussed. In the case of the machined crack, on the other hand, G_c was essentially independent of crack length with a mean value of 3.2 lb/in., which is about the same as reported values for the epoxy matrix alone [8]. From the observed difference in G_c between the natural and machined crack tests, the fiber bridging action can be seen to contribute significantly to fracture toughness parallel to the fibers of unidirectional S-glass composites. Toughness values for MOD I and MOD II graphite specimens were much lower than those of the S-glass specimens with natural cracks. The mean values of G_c obtained (see Fig. 7) were 2.30 and 1.88 lb/in. for MOD I and MOD II, respectively. Significantly, there appeared to be much less fiber bridging than with S-glass specimens, perhaps due to the higher stiffness of graphite fibers. Table 3 summarizes the mean fracture toughness results for all unidirectional specimens tested at α = 90°. Also

FIG. 4—*Fiber bridging action in a unidirectional S-glass/epoxy specimen,* (a) *with crack length at 0.8 W,* (b) *after complete fracture.*

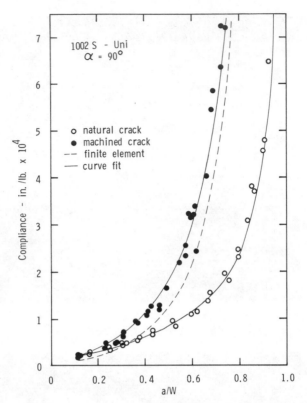

FIG. 5—*Compliance versus crack length curves for S-glass/epoxy specimens with machined and natural cracks.*

given in the table are the work of fracture values obtained from the area under the load-displacement curve and designated as W_f. There was reasonably good agreement between W_f and G_c, the latter tending to be slightly higher. In all fracture toughness tests conducted, there was considerable data scatter. The standard deviation of G_c ranged from 11 to 25 percent of the mean value. Variation within a single specimen was often greater than between two different specimens of the same material.

TABLE 3—*Mean fracture toughness values, unidirectional specimens (α = 90°).*

Material	G_c, lb/in.	W_f, lb/in.
S-glass/epoxy		
Natural crack	7.65	7.27
Machined crack	3.18	...
MOD I graphite/epoxy	2.30	1.97
MOD II graphite/epoxy	1.88	1.74

The work of fracture values were used to determine the effect of fiber orientation on toughness in S-glass specimens. In Fig. 8 these data are plotted against inclined crack length measured from the initial notch. In this plot are data from specimens of all the various fiber orientations. These plot roughly as a straight line corresponding to W_f = 6.85 lb/in., and no distinction can be made among the data on the basis of fiber orientation. Within the data spread there does not appear to be a variation in toughness with fiber orientation. This supports the hypothesis offered in Ref *3* that

$$G_c = G_I + G_{II} = \text{Constant} \qquad (4)$$

for unidirectional composites in which crack propagation is parallel to fibers. G_I and G_{II} are the strain energy release rates in the crack opening and forward shear modes, respectively. The crack direction is pre-determined by fiber orientation, and the relative contributions of G_I and G_{II} are fixed by this orientation and possibly by crack length; but the sum of the separate contributions of the two modes remains a material constant with crack extension.

One further observation was made in the unidirectional specimen tests. It was impossible to measure G_c for specimens with α = 0 as one of the

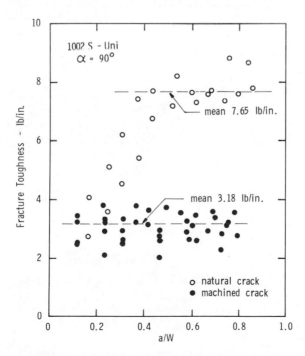

FIG. 6—*Variation of fracture toughness,* G_c, *with crack length in unidirectional S-glass/epoxy specimens.*

arms in the double cantilever region generally broke off because of the tendency for the crack to travel parallel to the fibers. Several attempts were made to propagate the crack across fibers in specimens of this orientation by bonding doublers to them in order to prevent crack growth parallel to the fibers. These attempts were unsuccessful and the only successful method found to propagate a crack across the fibers was to machine a deep side groove in a cross-ply specimen such that only two plies of the 8-ply laminate remained. Those two remaining plies were normal to plane of the crack. This method worked only with graphite specimens. G_c values based on the reduced thickness in the groove were obtained for two MOD II specimens and are shown in Fig. 7. The mean value observed was 355 lb/in., more than two orders of magnitude higher than for specimens with $\alpha = 90°$.

Cross-Ply Specimens

Not only was the behavior of cross-ply fracture specimens different from that of unidirectional specimens, but there was a marked difference in behavior between S-glass and graphite cross-ply specimens. In S-glass

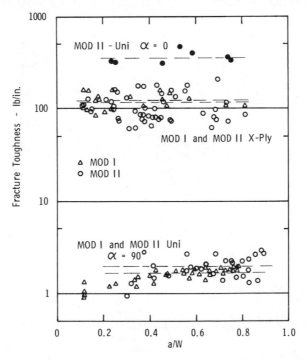

FIG. 7—*Variation of fracture toughness, G_c, with crack length in unidirectional and cross-ply graphite/epoxy specimens.*

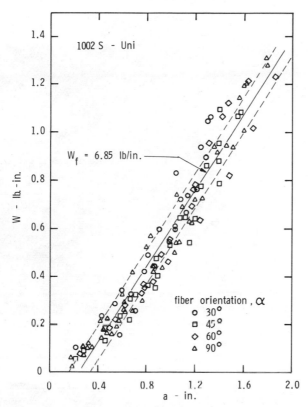

FIG. 8—*Work of fracture versus crack length in unidirectional S-glass/epoxy specimens having various fiber orientations.*

specimens some early cracking occurred at the notch tip at loads comparable to those at initial cracking in unidirectional specimens. After this, a system of superficial cracks parallel to the fibers in the various plies developed, and the load-displacement behavior became nonlinear in a way usually characteristic of gross plastic deformation. The damage zone was considerably larger than the plastic zone ahead of the crack tip in a metal specimen and tended to dominate subsequent behavior. Figure 9 shows such a zone developing in a specimen with the outer plies oriented at 45° to the load. In Fig. 9a the first crack is seen at the notch tip, having occurred at a load of about 170 lb. The photograph was taken subsequently at a load of 800 lb. A dye penetrant was used to improve contrast between the crack and specimen surface. In Fig. 9b the load has been increased to 1300 lb; but the initial crack has not extended; instead, the system of parallel, one-ply thickness cracks has developed. The corresponding load-displacement curve during this cracking sequence is seen in Fig. 10. Generally, this damage zone continued to spread with further

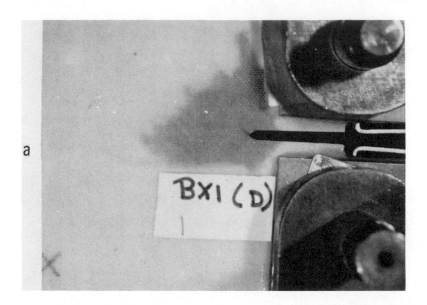

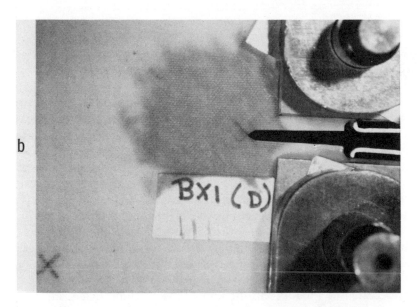

FIG. 9—(a) *Initial crack in a cross-ply S-glass/epoxy specimen (α = 45°);* (b) *System of parallel, one-ply deep cracks at increased load.*

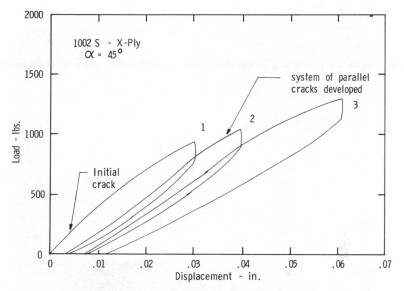

FIG. 10—*Load-displacement history for cross-ply of an S-glass/epoxy specimen.*

load increase without development and extension of a through crack. Since there was no crack propagation, no determination of G_c could be made for the S-glass/epoxy cross-ply specimens. The type of damage mechanism observed suggests that the usual fracture mechanics approach is inappropriate for these materials. The development of an alternative procedure would require a way of quantitatively evaluating the extent of the damage zone throughout the various plies.

The cross-ply MOD I and MOD II specimens behaved in a more brittle fashion than the S-glass/epoxy specimens. In general, a sharp crack was propagated from the notch; however, crack extension with increased load was frequently in a zig-zag direction, parallel at any time to one or the other ply directions. This is seen in Fig. 11a and b which show the crack at two different stages of development in a cross-ply MOD II specimen with a 45° orientation. Other damage mechanisms such as fiber debonding, ply delamination, and periodic splitting ahead of the crack in plies parallel to the load direction were also frequently observed. The load-deformation behavior was essentially linear even after damage occurred. The splitting observed occurred in tests in which the outer specimen plies were parallel to the load. Cracks in the outer plies occurred at regular intervals and were perpendicular to the main crack and usually accompanied by local delamination. In specimens with the outer plies perpendicular to the load such splitting occurred to a much lesser degree in the inner parallel plies due to constraint from the outer plies. The effect of the

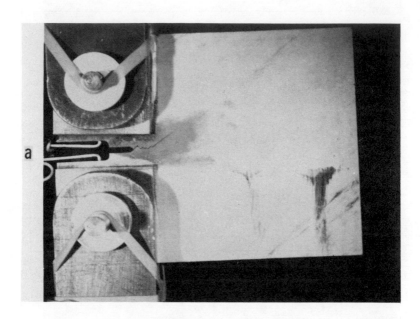

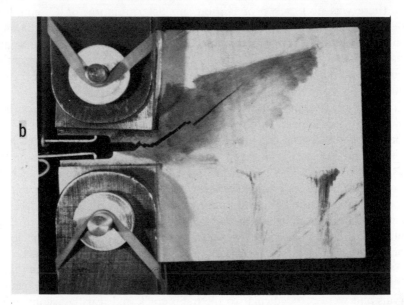

FIG. 11—*Crack development in a cross-ply graphite/epoxy specimen (α = 45°) at two different stages of loading.*

splitting was found to increase the overall specimen compliance, but there was no significant effect on the measured fracture toughness.

Figure 12 shows the compliance curves based on data for all MOD I and MOD II specimens. The finite element solution is shown as the dashed line; and in contrast to the case of unidirectional specimens, it predicts lower compliance values with crack length than were observed experimentally. This discrepancy may be due to the splitting and delamination in plies parallel to the load. In general, the finite-element predictions for all specimen types varied too widely from experimental compliance values to be used as an alternative calibration procedure. A reexamination of the finite-element model may be required to obtain compliance predictions more in line with observed values. Figure 7 shows the fracture toughness, G_c, as a function of crack length for all MOD I and MOD II specimens except those at $\alpha = 45°$ to be discussed later.

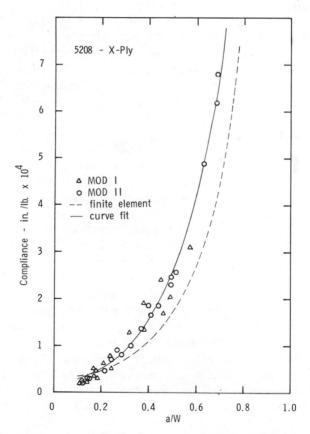

FIG. 12—*Compliance versus crack length curves for MOD I and MOD II cross-ply specimens ($\alpha = 0$ and $90°$).*

The mean value of G_c was 124 lb/in. for MOD I and 117 lb/in. for MOD II cross-ply specimens. There was no apparent dependence of G_c on crack length in either case. As with unidirectional specimens, there was wide data scatter, the standard deviation being about 15 percent of the mean. The variation was evident within a single specimen as well as from specimen to specimen and may be attributable to the random interaction of secondary failure modes discussed previously with the propagating crack. Another factor could be the random variation of fiber strength within the laminate.

The test results for the three types of MOD II specimens given in Fig. 7 indicate that the principal source of toughness in graphite composites is fracture across the fibers. G_c for unidirectional specimens with $\alpha = 0$ was about three times that for cross-ply specimens. Referring to Eq 1 to relate G to K at fracture in orthotropic laminates, and using the respective elastic properties in Table 1 for unidirectional and cross-ply graphite results in a mean value of K_c of 27.0 lb/in.$^2\sqrt{}$in. for cross-ply specimens and 51.3 lb/in.$^2\sqrt{}$in. for unidirectional specimens. The latter value is about twice that of the cross-ply laminate, which indicates that the stress intensity at fracture is nearly the same in the cross-ply laminate as in the unidirectional laminate. Fracture of plies at $\alpha = 90°$, delamination, and splitting in plies at $\alpha = 0$ would seem to contribute negligibly to overall fracture resistance of cross-ply specimens. On the other hand, fiber debonding and pull-out in plies at $\alpha = 0$ might be expected to make a significant contribution since these are mechanisms associated with fracture across fibers in graphite composites [4,8]. The mean work of fracture, W_f was found from the load-deformation curves to be 121 and 107 lb/in. for MOD I and MOD II cross-ply, respectively. These values agree well with the G_c values obtained by compliance calibration. In the case of cross-ply specimens oriented at 45° to the load direction, the compliance technique was not applicable for reasons previously discussed, but W_f was found to be 91 lb/in. for MOD I and 67 lb/in. for MOD II cross-ply. Thus, the work of fracture of cross-ply laminates, unlike the unidirectional case, varies with orientation with respect to the load.

The results obtained on graphite composites in this study have been compared with results obtained using other types of specimens in Table 4. The reference test methods cited use center-notched, slow bend, and tapered double-cantilever specimens. In the first of these, G_c was determined indirectly from K_c through Eq 1. In the slow bend test G_c was obtained from the area under the load-displacement curve. In general, the G_c values of this study compare well with center-notched specimen data for both MOD I and MOD II cross-ply graphite; but the W_f values are widely different from the slow-bend test results. The valid application of compact tension specimens to fracture characterization of composites is subject to the requirement that K_c and G_c are related through the elastic constants.

TABLE 4—*Fracture test results for graphite/epoxy.*

Material	G_c,[a] lb/in.	W_f,[a] lb/in.	G_c, lb/in.	Test Method (Ref)
Mod I (40% V_f)				
Unidirectional	2.3	2.0	2.9	center notched [8]
			3.0	slow bend [8]
Crossply	124	121	117	center notched [4]
MOD II (60% V_f)			153	slow bend [4]
Unidirectional	1.9	1.7	. . .	
Crossply	117	107	110	tapered DCB [4]
			115	center notched [4]
			68	slow bend [4]

[a] This study.

While there is wide data scatter and secondary fracture mechanisms are present in addition to crack propagation, this requirement appears to be reasonably well satisfied in the case of cross-ply graphite specimens.

Conclusions and Discussion

The compact tension fracture test gave valid results for unidirectional composite specimens with orientations other than $\alpha = 0$; however, the compliance calibration technique with this specimen is limited by practical consideration to $\alpha = 90°$. The test also gave valid results for graphite/epoxy cross-ply composites. It does not seem that the test method is applicable to cross-ply or angle-ply S-glass/epoxy composites because of the complex failure zone which develops in lieu of a sharp crack.

In unidirectional specimens, fracture toughness is dependent on crack length in the early stages of crack growth due to the development of the network of fibers bridging the crack plane behind the advancing tip. At certain crack lengths this network becomes fully effective and toughness remains constant with additional crack growth. This mechanism contributes a significant portion of the overall toughness of unidirectional composites, more so in S-glass/epoxy than in graphite/epoxy composites. The toughness of unidirectional composites is comparatively small as a result of the tendency for cracks to propagate parallel to, rather than across, fibers regardless of load orientation.

Cross-ply graphite specimens do not exhibit a dependence of toughness on crack length. Toughness values have considerable scatter from point to point within a given specimen due to random processes occurring in addition to crack propagation and due to material property variation. G_c values obtained from compact tension specimens of cross-ply graphite are reasonably consistent with K_c values determined by other test methods. This may be only a fortuitous coincidence in view of the complex failure behavior, and additional work is needed on various laminate configurations and stacking sequences before the application of linear elastic fracture mechanics to failure prediction of graphite composites is fully justified.

Acknowledgments

The authors gratefully acknowledge the assistance of Colin Freese of The Army Materials and Mechanics Research Center in developing the compliance curve fit program and of Agnes Travers in typing the manuscript.

References

[1] Wu, E. M. and Reuter, R. C., "Crack Extension in Fiberglass Reinforced Plastics," University of Illinois T and AM, Report No. 275, 1965.
[2] Wu, E. M., "Fracture Mechanics of Anisotropic Plates," *Composite Materials Work Shop,* Vol. I, Technomic, 1968.
[3] Lauraitis, K., "Tensile Strength of Off-Axis Unidirectional Composites," University of Illinois T and AM, Report No. 344, 1971.
[4] Phillips, D. C., "Fracture Mechanics of Carbon Fibre Laminates," *Journal of Composite Materials,* Vol. 8, April 1974.
[5] Mandell, J. F. et al, "Fracture of Graphite Fiber Reinforced Composites," Technical Report AFML-TR-73-142, July 1973.
[6] Paris, P. C. and Sih, G. C. in *Fracture Toughness Testing, ASTM STP 381,* American Society for Testing and Materials, 1970, pp. 30–83.
[7] Mostovoy et al in *Journal of Materials,* Vol. 2, No. 3, 1967, pp. 661–681.
[8] Beaumont, P. W. R. and Harris, R., "The Energy of Crack Propagation in Carbon Fibre-Reinforced Resin Systems," *Journal of Materials Science,* Nov. 1972.
[9] Bueckner, H. F., "The Propagation of Cracks and the Energy of Elastic Deformation," *Transactions,* American Society of Mechanical Engineers, 1958.

N. R. Adsit [1] *and J. P. Waszczak* [1]

Fracture Mechanics Correlation of Boron/Aluminum Coupons Containing Stress Risers*

REFERENCE: Adsit, N. R. and Waszczak, J. P., **"Fracture Mechanics Correlation of Boron/Aluminum Coupons Containing Stress Risers,"** *Fracture Mechanics of Composites, ASTM STP 593,* American Society for Testing and Materials, 1975, pp. 163–176.

ABSTRACT: The mechanical behavior of boron/aluminum near stress risers has been studied and reported. This effort was directed toward defining the tensile behavior of both unidirectional and $(0/\pm45)$ boron/aluminum using linear elastic fracture mechanics (LEFM). The material used was 5.6-mil boron in 6061 aluminum, consolidated using conventional diffusion bonding techniques.

Mechanical properties are reported for both unidirectional and $(0/\pm45)$ boron/aluminum, which serve as control data for the fracture mechanics predictions. Three different flawed specimen types were studied. Tension coupons containing circular centerholes, double edge notches, and center notches as well as control specimens were tested. The circular hole and double edge notched specimens were tested with various flaw sizes. In each case the series of specimens remained geometrically similar to eliminate variations in finite size correction factors. The center notched specimens were used to obtain conditions more in line with conventional plane-strain fracture testing.

The fracture data from these tests were reduced using two techniques. They both used conventional LEFM methods, but the existence of a characteristic flaw was assumed in one case and not the other. Both the data and the physical behavior of the specimens support the characteristic flaw hypothesis. Cracks were observed growing slowly in the $(0/\pm45)$ laminates, until a critical crack length was reached at which time catastrophic failure occurred.

KEY WORDS: fracture properties, composite materials, stresses, boron/aluminum coupons, laminates, fatigue (materials)

The emphasis in composite design is gradually shifting from achieving minimum weight designs at all costs to more cost-effective, damage tolerant structural designs. A damage tolerant structure must not only be able to effectively absorb energy locally at the point of damage initiation, but

*This work was supported jointly using IRAD and NASA contracted funds.

[1] Senior engineering metallurgist and senior structures engineer, Convair Division, General Dynamics Corp., San Diego, Calif. 92138.

must also be failsafe. A very efficient way of making a composite failsafe is to provide it the ability to arrest a potentially catastrophic crack. Most crack arrestment concepts will require data describing the fracture toughness of the composite material being considered.

Fracture toughness data is also required to explain the hole size effect observed in graphite/epoxy [1][2] and boron/aluminum [2]. By assuming that an inherent material flaw or region of intense energy governs failure in a composite, linear elastic fracture mechanics has been successfully used to correlate the experimental hole data [1,2]. A good physical understanding of the inherent flaw concept for graphite/epoxy has not yet been achieved.

The goal of this work is to determine the applicability of linear elastic fracture mechanics to boron/aluminum, to measure the fracture toughness of this material and to determine whether the inherent flaw concept is valid for the full range of boron/aluminum coupons containing stress risers.

Background

Material and Procedures

The material used for this study consisted of 5.6 mil boron filaments in a 6061 aluminum matrix. The as-received (or Condition F) diffusion bonded tape was purchased as consolidated 0-deg (unidirectional) and [0/±45]-deg sheets. Four types of straight-sided tension specimens with bonded doublers were manufactured from these sheets, as shown in Fig. 1. Several specimens served as control specimens, while the remaining contained either circular holes, edge notches, or center slots. The techniques of specimen fabrication are discussed in Ref 3.

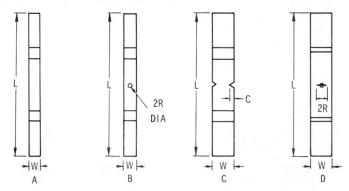

FIG. 1—*Various tension specimen configurations:* A = *control,* B = *center hole,* C = *edge notch, and* D = *center notch.*

---

[2] The italic numbers in brackets refer to the list of references appended to this paper.

All the tests were run at ambient temperature. The majority of specimens were tested on a Universal test machine in wedge action jaws utilizing a swivel joint to ensure load axiality. Specimens having widths greater than 1.0 in. were loaded directly in the jaws of the test machine. These specimens were carefully aligned by the technician to ensure axiality. No instrumentation was used on either the circular hole specimens or the edge notch specimens. A strain gage extensometer was used on the tension control specimens. A special strain-gage compliance gage was used for the center slotted specimens. The ultimate load was the only recorded data on the noninstrumented specimens, while a load-strain (or compliance) curve was recorded for the instrumented specimens.

Composite Fracture Mechanism

In a given composite laminate the fibers have a statistical distribution of strength. As the load applied to a laminate is increased, the weaker fibers fail and redistribute their load to the surrounding fibers by a shear transfer mechanism through the matrix. In a tension coupon containing a stress riser, the first fiber to fail in the laminate will be one of the weakest fibers in the immediate vicinity of the stress concentration. When that fiber fails, the strain energy released must be absorbed by the surrounding matrix and adjacent fibers. Load can continue to be applied after fiber failure as long as the strain energy released by that fiber can be absorbed by the surrounding matrix and fibers. The materials ability to support such slow crack growth by locally absorbing this released strain energy is a function of the magnitude of the local stress concentration, the local stress gradient, and the current crack length. Such slow crack growth has been observed in $(0/\pm45)_s$ Condition F boron/aluminum tension coupons containing circular holes.

In Fig. 2 a series of four photographs is presented which illustrates the details of this slow crack growth. The specimen shown was loaded to 85 percent of its predicted experimental failure load, which was determined by seven prior tests. The specimen was then unloaded, removed from the test machine, and the laminate was etched away layer by layer to produce the series of photographs. The crack length observed at 85 percent ultimate load was approximately 0.10 in., which theoretically represents a crack length of approximately 0.14 in. at ultimate load. Thus, a limited amount of physical evidence has been gathered which provides a physical explanation of the inherent flaw concept presented in Ref *1*. For the series of eight $(0/\pm45)_s$ coupons tested, cracks were observed growing at all four possible surface locations. While similar damage has not been observed in graphite/epoxy, a similar mechanism may in fact occur but may not be as noticeable, since the brittle epoxy does not neck down during crack growth, as does the aluminum.

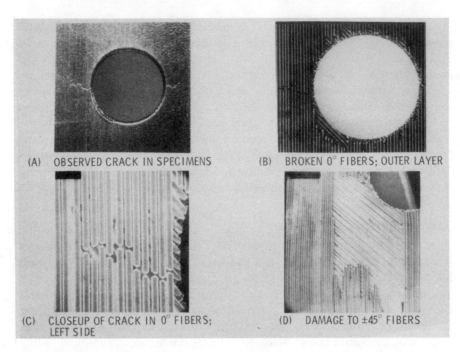

(A) OBSERVED CRACK IN SPECIMENS

(B) BROKEN 0° FIBERS; OUTER LAYER

(C) CLOSEUP OF CRACK IN 0° FIBERS;
LEFT SIDE

(D) DAMAGE TO ±45° FIBERS

FIG. 2—*Details of observed crack growth in (0/±45)ₛ Condition F boron/aluminum tension coupons.*

Results and Observations

The data obtained for the unidirectional material is summarized in Table 1 and plotted in Fig. 3. The (0/±45) laminate data is presented in Table 2 and Fig. 4. The test data clearly indicates that there is a specimen flaw size effect on the net section strength. The goal of the following analytical work is to understand the flaw size effect, attempt to use fracture mechanics to correlate the experimental data, and to show that the fracture toughness of a given boron/aluminum laminate is predictable and constant (that is, a material property).

Data Reduction

The first attempt at reducing the unidirectional material failure data was to directly use linear elastic fracture mechanics, as developed for isotropic homogenous materials, by assuming that the machined flaws (circular holes and edge notches) act as sharp cracks. In each case, the maximum lateral flaw dimension was used as the crack length. Plane-strain fracture toughness values were calculated for specimens containing center holes using Eq 1, and for the specimens with side notches using Eq 2 [4].

TABLE 1—*Test results of unidirectional boron/aluminum.*

Specimen	Hole Dia./Notch Depth 2R/c (in.)	Specimen Width (in.)	Failure Stress (net) (ksi)
	Tensile Control		
5.4.1-1		0.5	206.6
5.4.1-2			211.6
5.4.1-3			210.7
5.4.1-4			225.0
	Hole		
5.4.1-5	0.125	0.5	157.0
5.4.1-6	0.125		152.6
5.4.1-7	0.125		153.0
5.4.1-8	0.125		154.5
5.4.1-9	0.187	0.75	148.1
5.4.1-10	0.187		145.9
5.4.1-11	0.187		153.3
5.4.1-12	0.187		145.8
5.4.1-13	0.250	1.0	145.6
5.4.1-14	0.250		145.7
5.4.1-15	0.250		140.4
5.4.1-16	0.250		152.1
5.4.1-17	0.500	2.0	119.8
5.4.1-18	0.500		125.2
5.4.1-19	0.500		130.1
5.4.1-20	0.500		129.0
	Notch		
5.4.1-21	0.150	0.5	170.4
5.4.1-22	0.150		172.5
5.4.1-23	0.150		177.8
5.4.1-24	0.150		168.6
5.4.1-25	0.225	0.75	139.7
5.4.1-26	0.225		143.1
5.4.1-27	0.225		121.7
5.4.1-28	0.225		147.3
5.4.1-29	0.300	1.0	144.7
5.4.1-30	0.300		141.9
5.4.1-31	0.300		142.6
5.4.1-32	0.300		144.9
5.4.1-33	0.600	2.0	97.2
5.4.1-34	0.600		61.0
5.4.1-35	0.600		132.4
5.4.2-36	0.600		121.2
	Slits		
1	0.30	0.75	158.9
2	0.30	0.75	147.9
3	0.60	1.50	135.8

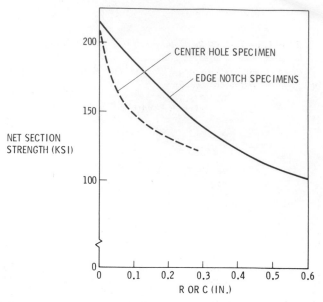

FIG. 3—*Tensile strength as a function of notch or hole size for unidirectional boron/aluminum.*

$$K_Q = Y_h \sigma \sqrt{R} \tag{1}$$

where
$$Y_h = 1.77 \left[1 - 0.1 \left(\frac{2R}{w} \right) + \left(\frac{2R}{w} \right)^2 \right]$$

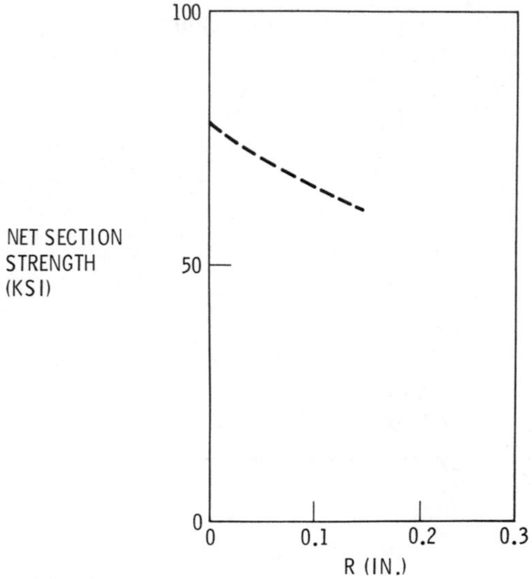

FIG. 4—*Tensile strength of 0/±45 boron/aluminum with circular holes.*

TABLE 2—*Test Results for 0/±45 boron/aluminum.*

Specimen	D or C[a]	Width	Failure Stress Net, ksi
Tensile Controls			
TC-1F	...	1.0	83.0
TC-2F	...	1.0	77.0
TC-3F	...	1.0	74.0
Circular Holes			
CH-1F	0.125	1.0	72.1
CH-2F	0.125	1.0	71.1
CH-3F	0.125	1.0	68.8
CH-4F	0.250	1.0	61.3
CH-5F	0.250	1.0	60.9
CH-6F	0.250	1.0	64.2

[a]D = diameter of circular hole; C = edge notch depth.

$$K_Q = Y_e \sigma \sqrt{c} \tag{2}$$

where $\quad Y_e = 1.98 + 0.36 \left(\dfrac{2c}{w}\right) - 2.12 \left(\dfrac{2c}{w}\right)^2 + 3.42 \left(\dfrac{2c}{w}\right)^3$

While the authors realize the limitations of using these equations in this manner, the results did serve as an interesting comparison to the inherent flaw analysis data. The calculated K_Q values from the unidirectional data have been plotted as a function of specimen width in Fig. 5. After

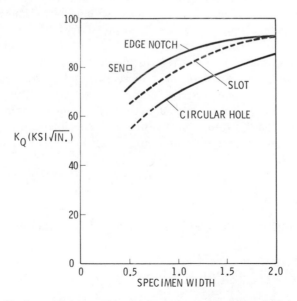

FIG. 5—*K_Q for unidirectional boron/aluminum as a function of specimen width.*

examination of the data, a second plot of K_Q versus the half crack length was made, and shown in Fig. 6. These data indicate a trend toward a value of K_Q for wide plates of approximately 92 ksi$\sqrt{\text{in}}$.

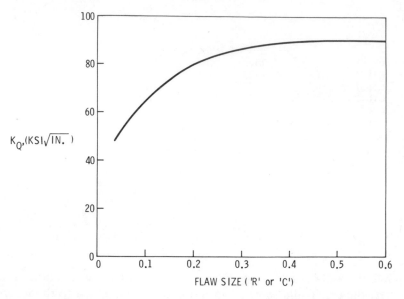

FIG. 6—K_Q *of unidirectional boron/aluminum as a function of flaw size.*

Assume now that both linear elastic fracture mechanics and the inherent flaw concept are applicable to composite materials. There are two material parameters which must be determined for the laminate before strength predictions can be made; the half length of the inherent flaw or characteristic crack, *a,* and the critical Mode I stress intensity factor for the laminate, K_Q. To determine these two unknowns, consider the following two independent tests: a simple tension coupon and a tension coupon containing a circular cutout both made from the same laminate. The fracture mechanics solutions for these two specimens are summarized in Fig. 7. The tension coupon containing an inherent flaw of length $2a$ is shown in Fig. 7a.

$$K_Q = \sigma^\infty \sqrt{\pi a} \tag{3}$$

The tension coupon containing a circular cutout with the inherent flaw is shown in Fig. 7b.

$$K_Q = \sigma_c^\infty \sqrt{\pi a} F(a/R) \tag{4}$$

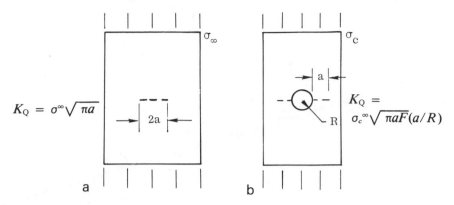

FIG. 7—*Two independent tests used to experimentally determine the composite fracture parameters a and K_Q. (a) Tension coupon containing an inherent flaw of length 2a, and (b) tension coupon containing a circular cutout with the inherent flaw.*

In both cases it is assumed that the coupons are infinitely wide with respect to the overall flaw size and that crack growth is in a direction perpendicular to the applied load. Therefore, the experimental failure stresses must first be corrected for the effects of finite size. Equations 3 and 4 can be used to calculate a and K_Q knowing $F(a/R)$, σ^∞, and σ_c^∞. Values for $F(a/R)$ are available in the literature [5] for isotropic materials. For laminates which are nearly quasi-isotropic these correction factors can be used. However, numerical solution methods should be used to analyze all other laminates.

If a nearly quasi-isotropic laminate is analyzed, the following procedure can be used to determine a and K_Q. Calculate $F(a/R)$ from Eq 5, which results from equating Eq 3 and Eq 4.

$$F(a/R) = \sigma^\infty/\sigma_c^\infty \tag{5}$$

Determine a/R using $F(a/R)$ from the table in Ref 5, where $F(a/R)$ is given as a function of a/R. Knowing R, the radius of the circular hole, a can be determined directly. By substituting a back into either Eq 3 or Eq 4, the value of K_Q can be determined.

An alternate method used by these authors was to iteratively perform numerical stress analyses of the two specimens illustrated in Fig. 7. The method used was to select a value of a based on visual observations during the static tests, set up computer models for the two problems illustrated in Fig. 7, numerically solve both for the stresses ahead of the crack, and derive two K_Q values, one for each of the specimens.

Utilizing Fig. 8, the Mode I crack opening stress σ_y, in the region directly ahead of the crack tip, along the line $\theta = 0$, is given by

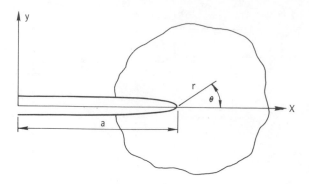

FIG. 8—*Crack tip stress field.*

$$\sigma_{y_{\theta=0}} = \frac{K_Q}{\sqrt{2\pi r}} \tag{6}$$

By plotting K_Q versus r/a on log-log paper, and best fitting the data with a line having a slope of $(-1/2)$, the value of K_Q can be determined using any $(\sigma_{y_{\theta=0}}, r/a)$ point on the line, since

$$\log \sigma_{y_{\theta=0}} = -1/2 \log(r/a) + \log K_Q - 1/2 \log(2\pi a) \tag{7}$$

A computer program described in Ref 6, which utilizes the boundary integral equation method (Ref 7), was used in the current work to perform the numerical analyses.

Numerical Results

Unlike the finite element method, where the entire body must be segmentized with elements, the two-dimensional boundary, integral equation method only requires the analyst to segmentize the boundaries of the specimen using straight line segments. The model used to represent a tension coupon containing a circular hole with symmetric radial cracks is shown in Fig. 9 for a typical specimen geometry. This grid is automatically transformed to the desired geometry in the computer program (Ref 6). The program predicts both K_I and K_{II} values for combined tension and bolt loadings. Only tension loadings were considered in this study.

The only specimens analyzed to date are the $(0)_6$ and $(0/\pm45)_s$ Condition F boron/aluminum tension coupons, both with and without circular cutouts. Typical stress results for the $(0)_6$ laminate, assuming a value for a of 0.099 in., are presented in Fig. 10. The material properties used for the

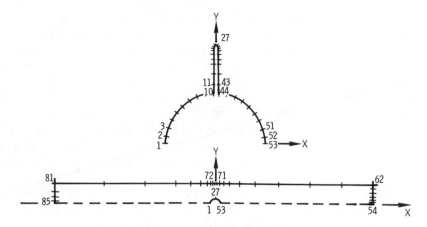

FIG. 9—*Boundary integral equation tension coupon model.*

unidirectional, boron/aluminum material were determined from a set of three specimens tested in Ref 2. They are as follows:

$$E_1 = 33.2 \times 10^6 \text{ psi}$$

$$E_2 = 22.7 \times 10^6 \text{ psi}$$

$$G_{12} = 8.91 \times 10^6 \text{ psi}$$

$$\nu = 0.26$$

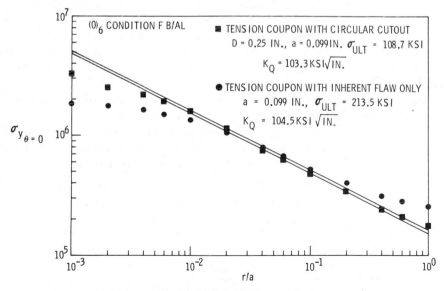

FIG. 10—$\sigma_{y_{\theta = 0}}$ *versus* r/a *for (0)₆ Condition F boron/aluminum tension coupons.*

Since the crack model has a finite radius of curvature at the crack tip, the stresses right at the crack tip do not exhibit the $\sqrt{r}$ singularity. Neither do the stresses away from the crack tip, since the crack no longer completely dominates the stress field. The stress data for this model normally satisfies the $\sqrt{r}$ singularity quite well in the range $0.01 < r/a < 1.0$. Since the stresses in the region near the crack tip ($r/a < 0.01$) do not approach infinity, but rather some finite value, the stresses in the region of interest ($0.01 < r/a < 1.0$), by equilibrium, are somewhat high due to the modeling error. The magnitude of the modeling error for the model used has been found to be approximately 14 percent [6,7].

Through a trial and error iterative procedure of estimating successive values for a and calculating values of K_Q, values of a and K_Q for the $(0)_6$ and $(0/\pm45)_s$ Condition F boron/aluminum laminates were determined. The results are summarized in Table 3.

TABLE 3—*Values of* a *and* K_Q *for* $(0)_6$ *and* $(0/\pm45)_s$ *Condition F boron/aluminum using numerical methods.*

Laminate	a (in.)	K_Q (ksi$\sqrt{}$in.)
$(0)_6$	0.105	106.7
$(0/\pm45)_s$	0.190	58.5

As an example of this procedure, consider the $(0)_6$ laminate. Boundary integral equation computer runs were made for an initial assumed value of $a = 0.0675$ in. using the experimentally determined failure loads, σ^∞ and σ_c^∞ (refer to Fig. 7). The resulting values of K_Q for the circular hole and inherent flaw specimens were 92.6 and 85.7 ksi$\sqrt{}$in. The third iteration K_Q values for an assumed value of $a = 0.099$ in. were 104.5 and 103.3 ksi$\sqrt{}$in. This procedure converged to a value of $K_Q = 106.7$ ksi$\sqrt{}$in. for a value of $a = 0.105$ in., as shown in Table 3.

For comparison, the results obtained using Eqs 3 and 4 and Bowie's isotropic correction factors are presented in Table 4. Data presented in Ref 8 was used to correct for the effects of finite specimen size.

TABLE 4—*Values of* a *and* K_Q *for* $(0)_6$ *and* $(0/\pm45)_s$ *Condition F boron/aluminum using Bowie's correction factors.*

Laminate	a(in.)	K_Q(ksi $\sqrt{}$in.)
$(0)_6$	0.083	109.0
$(0/\pm45)_s$	0.099	44.9

The corresponding value of a for $(0/\pm 45)_{2s}$ graphite/epoxy is approximately 0.040 in. [1].

Discussion and Recommendations

Both analytical methods considered result in predicted a values for $(0/\pm 45)_s$ Condition F boron/aluminum which are considerably larger than those for the $(0)_6$ laminate. The resulting fracture toughness of the $(0/\pm 45)_s$ laminate is in turn much smaller. These results were expected, based on strain energy transfer considerations. A crack can grow longer in a $(0/\pm 45)_s$ laminate than in a $(0)_6$ laminate, since a 0-deg ply can safely transfer more strain energy to adjacent ± 45-deg plies than to an adjacent 0-deg ply. Furthermore, the crack in a $(0/\pm 45)_s$ laminate grows only in the 0-deg plies, not the ± 45-deg plies. As shown in Fig. 2, the ± 45 plies near the crack tip are discontinuous and can absorb the transferred strain energy in a shear or fiber pullout mode, rather than in loading the brittle fibers in tension, as in the case in the $(0)_6$ laminate.

While slow crack growth has only been observed in the $(0/\pm 45)_s$ laminate, the pinging noises which are heard during loading of the $(0)_6$ laminates indicate that a similar successive fiber failure phenomenon may occur. Some indications of a pop-in were observed on the center slotted specimens which would also support a slow crack growth concept. A carefully controlled series of static tests using unidirectional material is planned to try to identify such damage accumulation or crack growth. From the data at hand, half-crack lengths on the order of 0.050 in. are expected.

The boundary integral equation results when compared to the predictions based on the Bowie solution show large differences, even for the nearly quasi-isotropic $(0/\pm 45)_s$ laminate. The problem here may involve more than just errors in the values used for $F(a/R)$. The numerical results show rather large variations in reaction loads on the left boundary of the tension coupon for an applied uniform stress boundary condition on the right-hand side. A detailed study needs to be performed to determine the appropriate boundary conditions for a tension test of an 8-in. or 10-in. by 1-in. composite laminate containing a quarter-in. diameter cutout, especially for strongly orthotropic laminates.

Conclusions

Several important observations were made and discussed regarding the applicability of linear elastic fracture mechanics to as-received boron/aluminum. First, boron/aluminum does exhibit a hole size effect similar to that previously reported for graphite/epoxy. Second, Mode I fracture toughness values of 106.7 ksi$\sqrt{\text{in.}}$ and 58.5 ksi$\sqrt{\text{in.}}$ were experimentally determined for the unidirectional and $(0/\pm45)_s$ as-received boron/aluminum laminates, respectively. And finally, the slow crack growth observed in the $(0/\pm45)_s$ tension coupons containing circular holes represents physical evidence supporting the inherent flaw concept.

Acknowledgments

The analysis and experimental data were generated using 1974 IRAD funds at General Dynamics, Convair Division. The authors wish to thank J. D. Forest, M. F. Miller, M. D. Weisinger, and C. R. Maikish for their valuable advice and assistance.

References

[1] Waddoups, M. E., Eisenmann, J. R., and Kaminski, B. E., *Journal of Composite Materials*, Vol. 5, 1971, p. 446.

[2] Waszczak, J. P. et al, "Structural Analysis Methods for Advanced Composites," CASD-ERR-73-029, General Dynamics Corp.., Convair Aerospace Division, Dec. 1973.

[3] Miller, M. F. and Schaefer, W. H., "Metal Matrix Fabrication Processes," SAMPE, Space Shuttle Materials, Vol. 3, Oct. 1973.

[4] Brown, W. F., Jr. and Srawley, J. E., *Plane Strain Crack Toughness Testing of High Strength Metallic Materials, ASTM STP 410*, American Society for Testing and Materials, 1967.

[5] Bowie, O. L., "Analysis of an Infinite Plate Containing Radial Cracks Originating from the Boundary of an Internal Circular Hole," *Journal of Mathematics and Physics*, Vol. 35, 1956.

[6] Waszczak, J. P., "Mode I and Mode II Stress Intensity Factors for Bolt Bearing Specimens Containing Symmetric Radial Cracks in Anisotropic Materials," Report SM-72-28, General Dynamics Contract P.O.-545073.

[7] Cruse, T. A., "Boundary—Integral Equation Solution Method," AFML-TR-71-268, Dec. 1971.

[8] Waszczak, J. P., "A Synthesis Procedure for Mechanically Fastened Joints in Advanced Composite Materials," AFML-TR-73-145, Volume III, Sept. 1973.

H. F. Brinson,[1] *M. P. Renieri,*[1] *and C. T. Herakovich*[1]

Rate and Time Dependent Failure of Structural Adhesives

REFERENCE: Brinson, H. F., Renieri, M. P., and Herakovich, C. T., **"Rate and Time Dependent Failure of Structural Adhesives,"** *Fracture Mechanics of Composites, ASTM STP 593,* American Society for Testing and Materials, 1975, pp. 177–199.

ABSTRACT: Studies on two adhesives (Metlbond 1113 and 1113-2) identified as having important applications in the bonding of composite materials are presented. A testing program to ascertain stress-strain, strain-rate, time, yield, and/or failure behavior of these materials in bulk form using uniaxial tensile constant strain-rate, creep, and relaxation tests is described. The stress-strain behavior of each material is shown to be significantly rate dependent. Further, it is shown that a rate dependent stress whitening (crazing) phenomenon occurs prior to either yield or fracture. A region of linear elasticity, a region of viscoelasticity, and the onset of yielding are identified in the stress-strain behavior. The linear elastic limit and the yield point are shown to be rate dependent and agree well with an empirical equation proposed by Ludwik. A creep to failure phenomenon is shown to exist and is correlated with a delayed yield equation proposed by Crochet. Analytical predictions based on a modified Bingham model are shown to agree well with experimental stress-strain strain-rate data. Analytical predictions based on a modified Ramberg-Osgood equation are also shown for comparison purposes. Information regarding rate and time dependent Poisson's ratios is also presented.

KEY WORDS: fracture properties, composite materials, stresses, adhesives, bonding strength

Adhesives are currently being used in a wide variety of structural applications. This is especially true for structures made using advanced composites. Composite joints formed by adhesive bonding have proven to be more efficient than those made by other methods which require penetration. The overall strength of an adhesively bonded structural composite cannot be predicted accurately unless the role of the adhesive joint is fully understood.

It has been pointed out that the process of adhesion can be divided into

---

[1] Associate professor, research assistant, and associate professor, respectively, Department of Engineering Science and Mechanics, Virginia Polytechnic Institute and State University, Blacksburg, Va. 24061.

two types; mechanical adhesion and specific adhesion [1].[2] The former describes the process of the adhesive solidifying in the pores of the two adherent surfaces, and the latter describes the process of attractive inter-molecular forces between molecules of even the smoothest solids. Further, it has been shown that the strength of adhesion depends primarily on the angle of contact between a liquid adhesive and the solid surfaces being bonded. Bowers et al [1] state that when the liquid film is very thin, the joint must fail in cohesion rather than adhesion. That is, failure is in the bulk phase rather than at the adherend/adhesive interface.

Adhesives that are used in composite bonding are frequently received in a partially polymerized thin film rather than in a liquid form. Thus, information relevant to the contact angle is difficult to obtain. Because of this fact and because bulk or cohesive failure is a likely failure mode, the present study is an effort to identify bulk or cohesive stress-strain, strain-rate, time, yield, and/or failure properties of two commercial adhesives. This is in contrast to the work of others regarding the visco-elastic behavior of adhesives [2].

A complete analysis of the stress distribution in adhesively bonded structural composite joints must include rate and time dependent material properties when these are significant. Adhesive materials, which are frequently molecular high polymers, generally exhibit significant rate and time dependence that must be considered in a reliable failure analysis. Therefore, the phenomenological behavior of the adhesives in bulk form is considered to be of prime importance in this study. The extent to which bulk properties can be related to properties in the bonded state is as yet undetermined. However, it is reasonable that if materials exhibit rate and time dependent failure characteristics in bulk form, they will exhibit similar behavior in the bonded state. Also, this study may give insight into rate and time dependent failure behavior of some matrix materials used in advanced composites as they are frequently similar in composition to the adhesives investigated herein.

Experimental Program

The experimental program consisted of constant strain (head) rate, creep, and relaxation tests on two commerically available adhesives, Narmco Whittaker's Metlbond 1113 and Metlbond 1113-2. Metlbond 1113 is a 100 percent solids,[3] modified epoxy film with a synthetic carrier cloth. Metlbond 1113-2 is the identical film without the carrier cloth. As this adhesive is normally used with the carrier cloth, tests were run on both materials to ascertain the behavior of the modified epoxy in

---

[2] The italic numbers in brackets refer to the list of references appended to this paper.
[3] This terminology implies the material contains no solvents or other additives.

both supported and unsupported form, that is, to establish the effect of the carrier cloth by comparison.

All tests were conducted on bulk specimens such as the failed specimen shown in Fig. 1. The specimens were cut from $\sim$ 0.140-in. ($\sim$ 0.335-cm) thick sheets which were laid up using 14 plys of film and cured according to manufacture's specifications in a platen press. The width of each specimen was $\sim$0.5 in. ($\sim$1.27 cm). Six plates of each adhesive were fabricated and either five or six specimens were cut from each plate. Over 40 specimens were tested.

Constant strain-rate tests were performed on an Instron testing machine using head rates ranging from 0.002 in./min (0.00508 cm/min) to 2 in./min (5.08 cm/min). For the strain-rate tests, each specimen was instrumented with an extensometer and both longitudinal and transverse electrical resistance foil-type strain gages. The extensometer was used to ascertain if

FIG. 1—*Typical failed specimen.*

heating or reinforcement of the electrical gages affected test results. Good correlation was obtained between the two methods for nearly the full range of strains. A small difference in strain values was obtained after local yielding (that is, the formation of crazing or microcracks), with the electrical gage giving slightly lower results. This behavior was attributed to the reinforcing effect of the electrical strain gage. The signals from the extensometer and the foil gages were amplified using a Vishay (Model BAM-1) bridge amplifier and were recorded on a Hewlett Packard (7100 B) dual-channel strip chart recorder. The bridge amplifiers were operated at reduced voltage which minimized strain gage heating effects and allowed recording of strains up to 10 percent.

Initially, two specimens from one panel and one specimen from a second panel of each material (1113 and 1113-2) were tested at the same strain rate. These tests established the repeatability of results for specimens from the same or different panels. In all cases differences of less than 2 percent were found in stress-strain behavior below fracture. Fracture stresses varied similarly but fracture strains were more random. Only one specimen was used for each of the remaining tests.

Creep tests were performed using a pneumatic test machine (manufactured by Allied Research Associates) which allowed rapid loading at a rate of about 20 in./min (50.8 cm/min). Loading was monitored using a Baldwin SR-4 (Type U-1) load cell with a Baldwin (Type L) strain indicator. Both longitudinal and transverse strains were recorded using the electrical strain gages and the instrumentation previously described.

Relaxation tests were conducted using a Twing-Albert test machine with the initial strain being applied at a rate of 20 in./min (50.8 cm/min). The same load cell and strain gage instrumentation as previously described was used.

Controlled environmental conditions of approximately 72°F and 75 percent relative humidity were used in all tests.

Experimental Results

The stress-strain behavior of Metlbond 1113 is shown in Fig. 2 for four different strain (head) rates. Linear elastic behavior with little rate effect was found for low stress levels. However, the linear elastic limit was found to be rate dependent. Above the linear elastic limit, significant rate effects were observed which could be attributed to viscoelastic behavior. The ultimate stress and the fracture stress were also found to be significantly rate dependent. As stated earlier, fracture strains, while rate dependent, appeared to be more random.

In the rate tests a stress-whitening phenomenon was observed to occur at stresses and strains well below ultimate or fracture levels. This stress-whitening phenomenon is similar to that reported by other investigators [3].

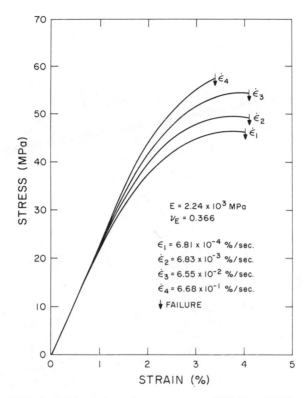

FIG. 2—*Stress-strain strain-rate response of Metlbond 1113.*

While detailed microscopic studies were not performed, it is believed that the stress whitening observed was a crazing phenomenon which is frequently observed in polymers [4]. The stress whitening may be seen in the photograph shown in Fig. 1. It should be noted that the fine cracks are essentially perpendicular to the loading direction. The time, strain level, and stress level, where it occurred in the rate tests, can be found in Table 1. The stress level for occurrance of stress whitening was rate dependent, but the strain level was nearly constant. It is felt that the stress-whitening effects observed can be attributed to crazing and that this process is evidence that a local damage or a local failure phenomenon occurs. This effect was observed in advance of gross fracture, but well beyond the linear elastic limit as indicated by results presented in Table 1 and Fig. 2. As such, it is an important characteristic of this material.

Table 1 gives further information regarding the properties found for both Metlbond 1113 and 1113-2 in the rate tests. Young's moduli and Poisson's ratios for the initial elastic region, and the stress at onset of crazing and the ultimate stresses may be found therein.

TABLE 1—Experimental results.

Material	Symbols for Fig. 8		Elastic Strain Rate $\dot{\varepsilon}$ (%/s)	Elastic Modulus $E \times 10^{-2}$ (MPa)	Elastic Poisson Ratio, ν	Failure Time, T^* (min)	Stress-Whitening Strain, ε_{sw} (%)	Stress-Whitening Stress, σ_{sw} (MPa)	Stress Whitening Time, T_{sw} (min)	Ultimate Stress, Y (MPa)	Symbols for Fig. 8	Stress, σ_0 (MPa)	Creep to Failure Time, T_F (min)
						Constant Strain Rate Properies						Creep Properties	
Metlbond 1113	8a	O	6.81×10^{-4}	21.51	0.351	96	3.30	45.57	75.0	46.3	8c ■	40.64	410
	8a	●	6.83×10^{-3}	22.75	0.382	10.44	3.32	49.64	4.0	50.0	8c □	42.79	260
	8a	□	3.35×10^{-2}	22.06	0.390	2.15	3.38	51.15	1.677	51.64	8c ●	47.22	26.75
	8a	△	6.55×10^{-2}	22.95	0.360	1.105	3.48	53.37	0.769	54.6	8c O	51.02	3.35
	8a	▽	6.68×10^{-1}	22.75	0.370	0.085	...	...	...	57.8	...	...	...
Metlbond 1113-2	8b	O	7.00×10^{-4}	20.06	0.380	159.50	3.78	39.23	84.0	39.0	8d □	39.09	54
	8b	●	6.75×10^{-3}	20.68	0.392	19.50	3.77	42.47	8.8	42.7	8d ●	41.02	14
	8b	□	3.40×10^{-2}	19.31	0.357	2.40	3.70	42.54	1.8	42.74	8d O	42.54	5.9
	8b	△	7.05×10^{-2}	20.33	0.343	1.633	3.68	45.37	0.883	46.0	...	...	...
	8b	▽	6.35×10^{-1}	20.68	0.366	0.147	...	...	...	53.6	...	...	...

Relaxation and creep results are shown in Figs. 3 and 4 for Metlbond 1113. For these tests the initial strains and stresses were purposely made larger than the linear elastic limit values found in the rate tests as little viscoelastic effects were expected below these levels. As may be seen, the results in Figs. 3 and 4 tend to confirm these expectations. However, it is obvious that significant viscoelastic effects were observed at relatively high stress levels, especially for short time periods. Figure 4 also shows a phenomenon that was anticipated, namely, a delayed failure phenomenon. That is, in a creep test delayed failure and fracture was observed to occur after sufficient time at a particular stress level. The time for fracture decreased with increasing stress level. These results are similar to the delayed yield phenomenon found for polycarbonate by Brinson [5]. Delayed stress whitening was also found to occur and is evidence that both local and gross failure and/or fracture modes are time dependent.

All the data presented to this point has been for Metlbond 1113 (with carrier cloth). Similar tests were conducted for Metlbond 1113-2 (without carrier cloth) and similar results were obtained. The results are shown in Figs. 5, 6, and 7. The only major difference found in the behavior of the

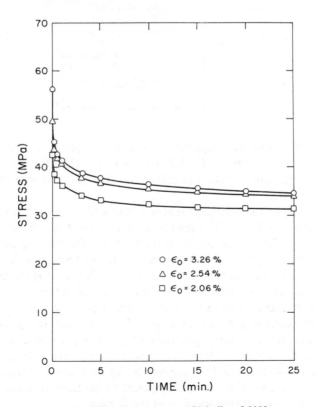

FIG. 3—*Relaxation response of Metlbond 1113.*

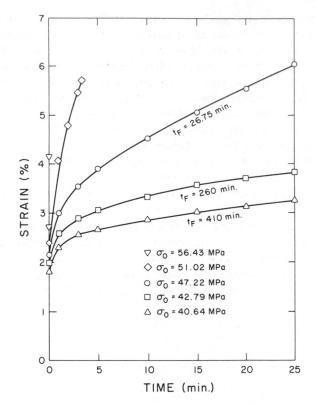

FIG. 4—*Creep response of Metlbond 1113.*

two materials was an expected somewhat higher ductility or more pronounced plastic flow in 1113-2 over that of 1113. The carrier cloth of 1113 tended to stabilize the material such that less random experimental results were obtained.

Poisson's ratio variations with strain rate and with time for both materials are shown in Fig. 8. The results are shown in terms of nondimensional time which is based upon the time required for fracture in each test. The fracture strains in the rate tests can be calculated from $\varepsilon = Rt$. The values for the fracture times are given in Table 1 for the various stress, strain, or strain-rate levels. The location in time (strain) at which stress whitening occurred in the strain-rate test is also shown in Figs. 8a and b. In the creep tests, stress whitening occurred during loading (that is, nearly instantaneously). It is felt that the occurrance of stress whitening is the reason for the general decrease in Poisson's ratios with strain and time. This phenomenon is also likely responsible for the lower initial values of Poisson's ratio in creep tests as opposed to strain-rate tests since stress whitening occurred during loading in the former.

The results shown in Fig. 8 on Poisson ratio variations together with creep, relaxation, and strain-rate data are adequate to determine the two material functions necessary for linear viscoelastic analysis if such is possible or desirable.

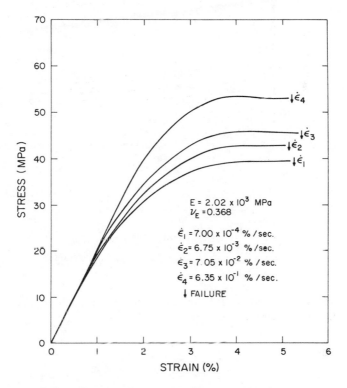

FIG. 5—*Stress-strain strain-rate response of Metlbond 1113-2.*

In the following discussion, the elastic limit stress, θ, and the elastic limit strain, ε_0, have been defined as the stress and strains separating the linear elastic region from the viscoelastic region. In other words these values of ε_0 and θ were taken to be the upper limit of linearity for each particular rate from data such as that shown in Fig. 2. This limit of linearity should not be confused with a limit of material linearity. Further, the yield stress, Y, has been defined as the ultimate stress. While these definitions are to some extent arbitrary, they do provide for consistant comparison of experimental results for rate and time dependent failure directly with theories which were proposed strictly for yield behavior such as those of Ludwik [6] and Crochet [7]. It is felt that regardless of the definition used for yielding, similar comparisons could be made.

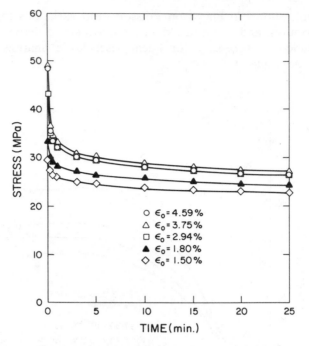

FIG. 6—*Relaxation response of Metlbond 1113-2.*

As proposed by Ludwik [6] the variation of yield stress, σ_{yp}, with strain rate, $\dot{\varepsilon}$, may be written in the form

$$\sigma_{yp} = \sigma'_{yp} + \sigma' \log \frac{\dot{\varepsilon}}{\dot{\varepsilon}'} \qquad (1)$$

where σ'_{yp}, σ', and $\dot{\varepsilon}'$ are material constants.

If the same form is assumed for the variation of elastic limit stress and strain, and yield stress with strain rate, the expressions may be written

$$\theta = \theta' + \phi \log \frac{\dot{\varepsilon}}{\dot{\varepsilon}'} \qquad (2)$$

$$\varepsilon_0 = \varepsilon'_0 + \alpha \log \frac{\dot{\varepsilon}}{\dot{\varepsilon}'} \qquad (3)$$

$$Y = Y' + \sigma' \log \frac{\dot{\varepsilon}}{\dot{\varepsilon}'} \qquad (4)$$

where additional material constants are defined accordingly.

Figure 9 shows a comparison of experimental results for ϕ and ε_0 as a function of $\dot{\varepsilon}$ compared with Eqs 2 and 3, respectively. It may be observed that the equations fit the experimental data quite well and could be used to interpolate the data for intermediate strain rates. However, Ludwik's equation with the constants as defined is not likely to be valid for significantly higher strain rates.

The variation of the yield stress (ultimate stress) with strain rate is shown in Fig. 10 for both Metlbond 1113 and 1113-2. Again, the results compare favorably with Eq 4.

It might be noted that in both Figs. 9 and 10 the results have been correlated to initial elastic strain rate. This was done because the tests which were conducted were constant head-rate tests and not constant strain-rate tests. Actual strain rates were nearly constant in the gage region until stress whitening occurred after which rates tended to change slightly.

A failed specimen is shown in Fig. 1. This failure is typical of all failures observed during this investigation. The stress whitening can be observed in the figure. The fracture surface was perpendicular to the loading axis and had the general appearance of a brittle tensile fracture.

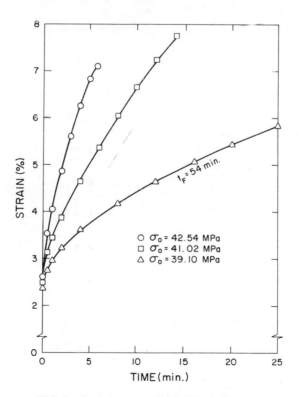

FIG. 7—*Creep response of Metlbond 1113-2.*

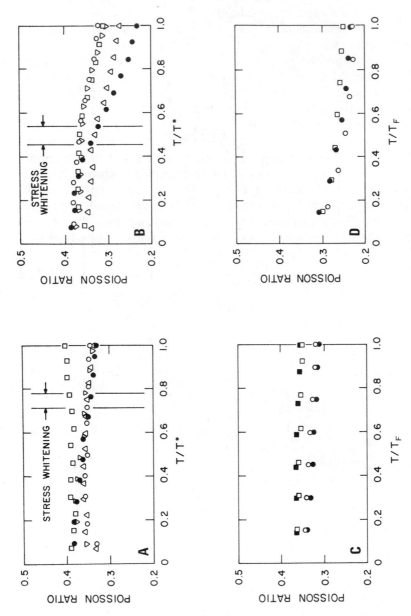

FIG. 8—*Variation of Poisson ratios with time:* (a) *constant strain-rate loading (Metlbond 1113),* (b) *constant strain-rate loading (Metlbond 1113-2),* (c) *creep loading (Metlbond 1113), and* (d) *creep loading (Metlbond 1113-2). See Table 1 for symbol identification.*

Essentially no permanent necking was observed nor was there evidence of slip bands as have been observed in polycarbonate.

Analytical Considerations

In any analytical solution of a specific boundary value problem it is necessary to provide a stress-strain characterization of the material under investigation. Also, yield, failure, and/or fracture need to be defined in rational mathematical terms. As has been demonstrated, Metlbond 1113 and 1113-2 exhibit a region of linear elasticity and a region of visco-elasticity followed by a small amount of flow at the ultimate stress prior to eventual fracture. Thus, it is desirable to formulate a simple mathematical model which will describe as many of these features as possible. A simple modified Bingham mechanical model for this purpose has been proposed by Brinson [5, 8]. With this model and a theory for delayed yielding proposed by Crochet [7], it was possible to effectively characterize many of the properties of polycarbonate.

The rheological equations for the modified Bingham model, which is shown in Figs. 11 and 12, can be written as

$$\varepsilon = \sigma/E, \quad \text{for} \quad \sigma < \theta$$

$$\dot{\varepsilon} = \frac{\sigma}{E} + \frac{\sigma - \theta}{\mu}, \quad \text{for} \quad \theta < \sigma < Y \tag{5}$$

where E is Young's modulus, and μ is the viscosity coefficient. A stress such that $\sigma > Y$ is not allowed. For a constant strain-rate test, that is, $\varepsilon = Rt$ and $\dot{\varepsilon} = R$, the solution of Eq 5 can be written as

$$\sigma(\varepsilon) = E\varepsilon, \quad \text{for} \quad 0 < \sigma < \theta$$

$$\tag{6}$$

$$\sigma(\varepsilon) = \theta + ER\tau[1 - e^{-(\varepsilon - \varepsilon_0)/R\tau}], \quad \text{for } \theta < \sigma < Y$$

where R is the strain rate, τ is the relaxation time, and ε_0 is the elastic limit strain defined previously. It may be observed that Eq 6 for the modified Bingham model allows for a linear elastic region, a linear visco-elastic region and a plastic region successively. Also, the yield stress, Y, in the model is obviously both rate and time dependent. Thus, the model can be used to describe a material which possesses rate dependent, creep, relaxation and delayed yield, or failure behaviors such as those previously described for Metlbond 1113 and 1113-2.

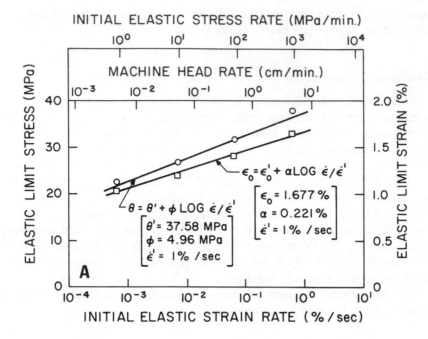

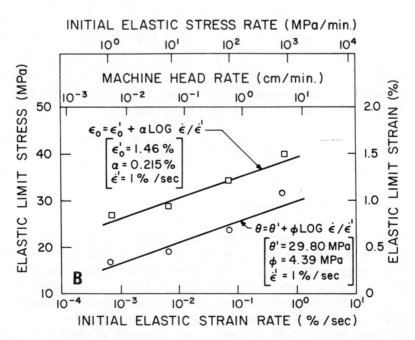

FIG. 9—*Variation of elastic limit stress and strain comparison with Ludwick's equation:* (a) *Metlbond 1113, and* (b) *Metlbond 1113-2.*

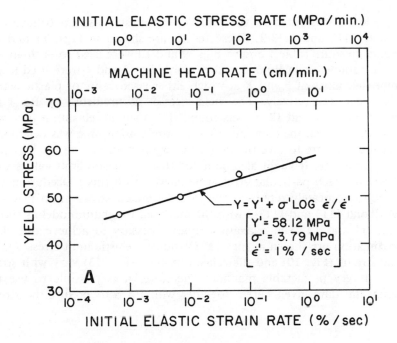

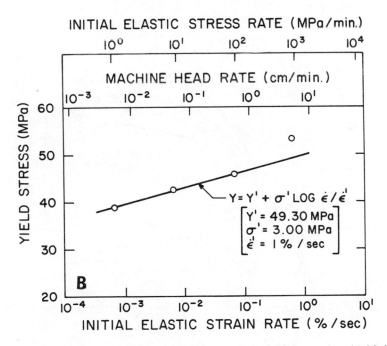

FIG. 10—*Variation of yield stress and comparison with Ludwick's equation:* (a) *Metlbond 1113, and* (b) *Metlbond 1113-2.*

Equation 6 was fitted to the rate dependent stress-strain behavior of Metlbond 1113 and 1113-2. These results are shown in Figs. 11 and 12. The data given in Table 1 and in Figs. 9 and 10 were used to evaluate the material parameters in Eq 6. In other words Eqs 2 and 4 were used to determine the values of θ and Y at which either viscoelastic or plastic action would occur, respectively. The yield stresses as predicted by Eq 4 are shown in Figs. 11 and 12. It was found that a single relaxation time was inadequate to fit all the data. As a result, a relaxation time was determined for each strain rate to give the best fit over the entire curve for that particular strain rate. It might also be noted that the elastic limit values were different for each particular strain-rate curve. With this procedure it was possible to accurately represent the rate dependent stress-strain behavior of Metlbond 1113 and 1113-2 with the modified Bingham model as shown in Figs. 11 and 12. The relaxation times necessary to achieve this close approximation are shown in Fig. 13. Obviously, elastic limit stresses (Fig. 6) and strains (Fig. 10) and the relaxation time (Fig. 13) vary with strain rate in a very predictable manner. Therefore, it is possible to use the experimental data given herein together with Eq 6 to predict the stress-

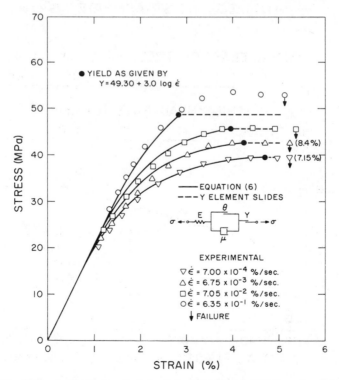

FIG. 11—*Stress-strain strain-rate behavior of Metlbond 1113-2 and comparison of the modified Bingham model.*

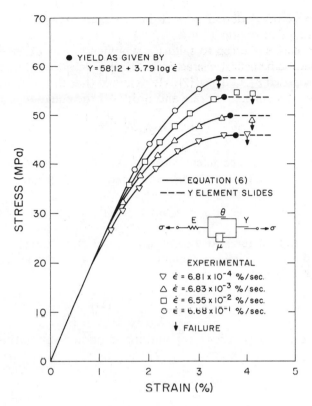

FIG. 12—*Stress-strain strain-rate behavior of Metlbond 1113 and comparison with the modified Bingham model.*

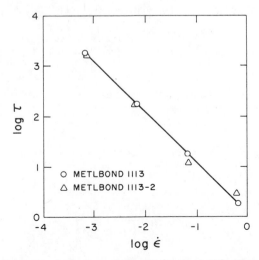

FIG. 13—*Relaxation time versus strain rate for the modified Bingham model.*

strain response of Metlbond 1113 and 1113-2 for an arbitrary strain rate within the range of test data.

As stated earlier a creep to failure phenomenon was observed. A possible rational mathematical characterization of a delayed yield phenomenon has been proposed by Crochet [7]. He assumed that the yield stress would increase for increasing strain rate and proposed the equation

$$Y(t) = A + B \exp(-C\chi) \tag{7}$$

where $Y(t)$ is a time dependent yield stress; A, B, and C are material constants; and χ is a time dependent material property given by

$$\chi = [(\varepsilon_{ij}{}^{v} - \varepsilon_{ij}{}^{E})(\varepsilon_{ij}{}^{v} - \varepsilon_{ij}{}^{E})]^{\frac{1}{2}} \tag{8}$$

In Eq 8 $\varepsilon_{ij}{}^{v}$ and $\varepsilon_{ij}{}^{E}$ refer to viscoelastic and elastic strains, respectively, and repeated indices indicate summation. For creep in uniaxial tension, Eq 8 can be written as

$$\chi = [(\varepsilon_{11}{}^{v} - \varepsilon_{11}{}^{E})^2 + (\varepsilon_{22}{}^{v} - \varepsilon_{22}{}^{E})^2 + (\varepsilon_{33}{}^{v} - \varepsilon_{33}{}^{E})^2]^{\frac{1}{2}} \tag{9}$$

Equation 5 can be solved for creep and the solution can be written

$$\varepsilon(t) = \frac{\sigma_0 - \theta}{\mu} t + \frac{\sigma_0}{E} \tag{10}$$

where $\sigma(t) = \sigma_0 H(t) > \theta$, $H(t)$ represents the unit step function, and t is time. The second term in Eq 10 represents elastic behavior. Thus, the term $(\varepsilon_{11}{}^{v} - \varepsilon_{11}{}^{E})^2$ in Eq 9 can be written as

$$(\varepsilon_{11}{}^{v} - \varepsilon_{11}{}^{E})^2 = \left[\frac{\sigma_0 - \theta}{\mu} t\right]^2 \tag{11}$$

If a constant Poisson's ratio (v) is assumed, the second and third terms of Eq 9 can be written as

$$(\varepsilon_{22}{}^{v} - \varepsilon_{22}{}^{E})^2 = (\varepsilon_{33}{}^{v} - \varepsilon_{33}{}^{E})^2 = v^2 \left[\frac{\sigma_0 - \theta}{\mu} t\right]^2 \tag{12}$$

Thus, Eq 9 becomes

$$\chi = \frac{\sigma_0 - \theta}{\mu} t \left[1 + 2v^2\right]^{\frac{1}{2}} \tag{13}$$

and by using this result, Eq 7 becomes

$$Y(t') = A + B \exp [-K(\sigma_0 - \theta)t']$$ (14)

Where $K = C(1 + 2\nu^2)^{1/2}/\mu$ is a constant containing various material parameters. In a creep test with $\sigma > \theta$, $Y(t)$, and σ_0 are identical. Hence

$$Y(t') = A + B \exp\{- K[Y(t') - \theta]t'\}$$ (15)

and t' represents the time for creep to yield to occur under constant stress.

The material constants, A, B, and K, were determined for Metlbond 1113 and creep to failure times for different stress levels were calculated according to Eq 15. The results are shown in Fig. 14 together with the experimental data. As may be observed, close correlation between measured and predicted values was found.

As an empirical Ramberg-Osgood equation is often used to characterize stress-strain properties, it was felt this procedure should also be considered for comparison purposes. The Ramberg-Osgood equation can be written as

$$\varepsilon = \frac{\sigma}{E} + K\sigma^n$$ (16)

where the first and second terms represent elastic and plastic strains, respectively, and where E, K, and n are material parameters [9].

McLellan [10] has modified Eq 16 for rate dependent materials by noting that for many materials n is invariant with strain rate and K and E are simple functions of strain rate such that

$$E = c\dot{\varepsilon}^d; \text{ and } K = a\dot{\varepsilon}^b$$ (17)

where a, b, c, and d are constants [10]. Therefore, Eq 16 can be written as

$$\varepsilon = \frac{\sigma}{c\dot{\varepsilon}^d} + a\dot{\varepsilon}^b\sigma^n$$ (18)

Variations in E are assumed to be due to viscoelastic effects while variations in K and n are assumed to be due to work hardening characteristics.

All the material parameters shown in Eqs 17 and 18 were found for Metlbond 1113 and 1113-2. Log-log plots of stress against plastic strain with strain rate as a parameter were made. The geometric slope of such a curve gives the value of n. For the adhesives investigated, variations of

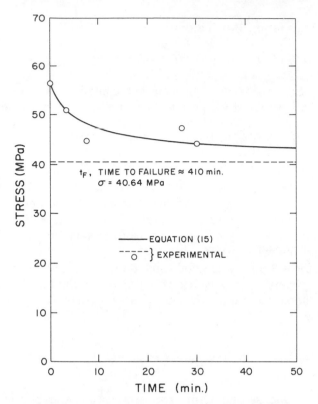

FIG. 14—*Comparison of creep to yield data and theory.*

n with strain rate were found and an average value was used. Knowing the value of n, the value of k was determined for each strain rate as the intercept of a log ε_p-log σ plot. Parameters a, b, c, and d were then determined emperically to give the best fit for the experimental data. These results are compared with the measured values in Figs. 15 and 16. As in Figs. 11 and 12, the values of the yield stresses as predicted by Eq 4 are also shown. It may be observed that behavior of 1113 can be approximated reasonably well with a modified Ramberg-Osgood equation while the behavior of 1113-2 cannot. The closer agreement with 1113 over 1113-2 is probably due to the fact that the parameter n varied much less with strain rate in the former than in the latter.

Discussion

The stress-strain, strain-rate, time, yield, and/or failure behavior of two structural adhesives used in composite applications has been presented. It has been shown that each material, Metlbond 1113 and 1113-2, displays a region of nearly linear elastic behavior and a region of viscoelastic behavior followed by a region of flow and fracture. A stress whitening or crazing phenomenon which was observed is evidence of early local damage. This damage plays a vital role in subsequent experimental observations of material properties. It is felt that this phenomenon alone may control eventual flow and fracture of each of these materials and may be indicative of similar behavior of other viscoelastic polymer adhesives or composite matrix materials.

A delayed failure phenomenon has been demonstrated and it has been shown that a technique proposed by Crochet coupled with a modified Bingham model characterization can successfully be used as a predictive technique. It should be noted that a somewhat different definition of the Parameter χ has been used herein as opposed to that used in Ref 5. The definition given in Eq 13 results in a correct form for $Y(t')$ in Eq 15 and conforms to Crochet's postulate.

It has been shown that a modified Bingham model can be used to quite accurately predict stress-strain strain-rate behavior of Metlbond 1113 and 1113-2. For this characterization, values of elastic limit stress and yield

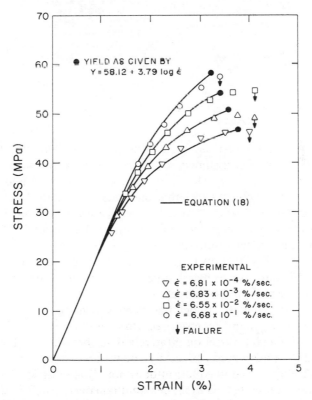

FIG. 15—*Stress-strain strain-rate behavior of Metlbond 1113 and comparison with the modified Ramberg-Osgood model.*

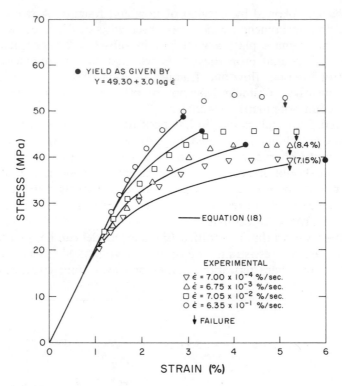

FIG. 16—*Stress-strain strain-rate behavior of Metlbond 1113-2 and comparison with the modified Ramberg-Osgood model.*

stress (ultimate stress) were assumed to be rate dependent. In other words Ludwik's equation was assumed to define the onset of viscoelastic and plastic action, respectively. This is in contrast to the procedures used in Refs 5 and 8. Even with this different approach it was still found necessary to use a variable relaxation time. It is appropriate to note here that a limited spectrum of constant relaxation times, that is, multiple Bingham elements, give no better results than a single constant relaxation time [7]. That is, a variable relaxation time is necessary and is likely indicative of nonlinear processes. Nevertheless, the procedure used has been demonstrated to be a useful predictive technique.

The modified Bingham model has been shown to agree with experimental data better than the modified Ramberg-Osgood equation. Also, the modified Bingham model qualitatively describes creep, relaxation, and delayed failure phenomena by easily identifiable parameters while the modified Ramberg-Osgood equation does not. Quantitative features of all these separate processes cannot be simultaneously predicted with the Bingham approach. Surely, the inclusion of nonlinear elements or other possibilities should be explored.

In order to establish unloading characteristics of Metlbond 1113 and 1113-2 in the viscoelastic and plastic regions, additional testing should be performed. Also, it is likely that the fact that the tests used were constant head rate, constant load, and constant displacement as opposed to constant strain-rate, creep, and relaxation tests significantly affected the results. Attempts should be made to correct these deficiencies. Efforts should also be undertaken to clearly identify nonlinear responses and might be accomplished using the procedures discussed by Schapery [11] and Lockett [12]. Nonlinear viscoelastic behavior would also effect the interpretation of either failure or fracture as suggested by Knauss [13]. In addition, temperature and other environmental effects are likely to be very important. All of these items are under study.

Acknowledgments

The financial support for this work provided by NASA Grant 47-004-090 is gratefully acknowledged. The materials used herein were generously donated by NARMCO Whittaker Corp. Further, the technical assistance and the many helpful discussions of J. G. Davis, Jr. of NASA-Langley is deeply appreciated.

References

[1] Bowers, R. C. and Zisman, W. A. in *Engineering Design for Plastics,* E. Baer, Ed., Reinhold Book Corp., New York, 1964, pp. 689–741.
[2] *Recent Advances in Adhesion,* L. H. Lee, Ed., Gordon and Breach, New York, 1973.
[3] Shoulberg, R. H. and Lang, E. R., *Experimental Mechanics,* 1962, p. 271.
[4] Hull, D. in *Deformation and Fracture of High Polymers,* H. H. Kausch et al, Eds., Plenum Press, New York, 1973, p. 171.
[5] Brinson, H. F. in *Deformation and Fracture of High Polymers,* H. H. Kausch et al, Eds. Plenum Press, New York, 1973, p. 397.
[6] Ludwik, P. G., *Elemente der Technologischen Mechanik,* J. Springer, Berlin, 1909, p. 9.
[7] Crochet, M. J., *Journal of Applied Mechanics,* Vol. 33, 1966, p. 326.
[8] Brinson, H. F. and DasGupta, A., "The Strain Rate Behavior of Ductile Polymers," SESA paper No. 2256, presented at the SESA Fall Meeting, Indianapolis, Ind., 16–19 Oct. 1973.
[9] Ramberg, W. and Osgood, W. R., "Description of Stress-Strain Curves by Three Parameters," NACA TN 902, April 1943.
[10] McLellan, D. L., "Constitutive Equations for Mechanical Properties," AIAA, Vol. 5, No. 3, 1966.
[11] Schapery, R. A., *Polymer Engineering Science,* 1969, pp. 295–310.
[12] Lockett, F. J., *Nonlinear Viscoelastic Solids,* Academic Press, 1972.
[13] Knauss, W. G., "The Mechanics of Polymer Fracture," *Applied Mechanics Reviews,* 1973, pp. 1–17.

N. M. Bhatia[1] *and R. M. Verette*[1]

Crack Arrestment of Laminated Composites

REFERENCE: Bhatia, N. M. and Verette, R. M., **"Crack Arrestment of Laminated Composites,"** *Fracture Mechanics of Composites, ASTM STP 593,* American Society for Testing and Materials, 1975, pp. 200–214.

ABSTRACT: In this paper the potential of the buffer strip concept for providing fracture control in graphite/epoxy laminated composite panels subjected to uniaxial tension static and fatigue loads is evaluated. The specific buffer strip design consists of replacing the 0-deg and 90-deg plies in a $\pi/4$ laminate with ±45-deg plies along strips parallel to the uniaxial load direction. A number of specimens were fabricated and tested. The specimens were 8 by 20-in. panels of 8-ply $(0, \pm45, 90)_s$ Thornel 300/SP286 graphite/epoxy laminates. Two 1-in. wide buffer strips were symmetrically placed 2 in. apart (3 in. center-to-center) and parallel to the longer sides of the panels. Initial flaws consisting of slits and circular holes of various sizes and orientations were machined at the midsection between the two buffer strips. Initial fracture and ultimate failure strengths of the panels were determined. In addition, several panels were fatigue cycled prior to static failure to assess the influence of fatigue loads on post-fatigue performance.

The static tests of the panels not previously fatigue tested showed that crack arrestment occurred when the initial flaw size exceeded 0.50 in. That is, the crack arrest capability was found to depend on the initial flaw size. For panels with 0.75 and 1.00-in. flaws, an initial fast crack was arrested in the buffer strips and the panels subsequently withstood approximately 20 percent more load. The crack initiation load for the panels which were previously fatigue cycled increased by approximately 10 percent as compared to the crack initiation load for an identical panel not previously fatigued. The improvement is attributed to development of zones of crazing and delamination in the crack tip region during fatigue cycling which reduce the local stiffness and the stress concentration. Fractographic examination of the failure surfaces confirmed the existence of this zone.

KEY WORDS: composite materials, laminates, fracture strength, crack propagation, cyclic loads, failure, fatigue (materials)

Advanced composite laminated structures under static and service loads respond with quasi-brittle modes of failure which are typically catastrophic. To prevent the occurrence of catastrophic failures due to normally occurring

[1] Engineering specialists, Northrop Corporation, Aircraft Division, Hawthorne, Calif. 90250.

service loads applied to a flawed structure, where the flaws may occur during manufacturing or during service, one approach is to design advanced composite laminated structures to be fail-safe. Since advanced composite structures show no evidence of slow stable crack growth under cyclic loading, design concepts are required to arrest a fast crack propagating under load and initiating from a damaged area. The buffer strip concept has been proposed in the literature [1][2] for arresting a fast crack initiating from a damaged area in boron/epoxy panels. The buffer strip concept consists of designing laminates with strips of varying stiffness and fracture toughness so as to reduce the stress intensity at the tip of a running crack as it enters the buffer strip zone. The amount of reduction in stress intensity should be enough for the buffer strip at act as a crack stopper.

At present, analytical solutions are not available for exact determination of the stress intensity factors for orthotropic panels with buffer strips, although numerical techniques are available to yield approximate solutions. Therefore, stress intensity factors for the infinite panel geometry have been used [1] as an approximation for the finite-width buffer strip panel. Also, methods have been suggested in the literature [2] to calculate upper and lower bounds for the stress intensity factor when the crack tips are in the primary laminate, in the buffer strips, and at the interfaces.

Application of the buffer strip concept to boron/epoxy laminates has been studied experimentally for panels subjected to static test loads [1]. However, the buffer strip concept has not been systematically applied to graphite/epoxy laminates subjected to static and fatigue loads in a manner so that the conclusions of Ref 1 can be checked for graphite/epoxy laminates. In this paper the potential of the buffer strip concept for providing fracture control of initially flawed graphite/epoxy laminated composite panels subjected to uniaxial tension static and fatigue loads is evaluated. Experimental data are presented for a specific panel geometry. The extension of the test results to the design of panels with multiple buffer strips is also presented.

Description of Test Program

The test program was designed to assess the potential of the buffer strip concept in providing fracture control of initially flawed graphite/epoxy laminated composite panels under uniaxial static and cyclic loads. The design of the graphite/epoxy panels with buffer strips consists of replacing the 0-deg and 90-deg plies in a $\pi/4$ laminate with ±45-deg plies in the uniaxially loaded panel. To evaluate the potential of the buffer strip design, 12 identical panels were fabricated using 8-ply $(0, \pm45, 90)_s$ laminates of

[2] The italic numbers in brackets refer to the list of references appended to this paper.

high strength graphite/epoxy (Thornel 300/SP286) material. The overall panel geometry and laminate construction is shown in Fig. 1. The panels

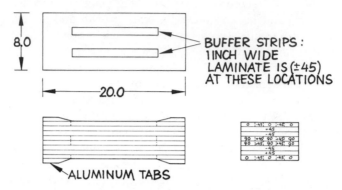

FIG. 1—*Test panel configuration, 8-ply π/4 laminate with ±45-deg buffer strips.*

were 8-in. wide by 20-in. long with two 1-in. wide buffer strips of ±45 deg laminates spaced 2 in. apart. Initial flaws consisting of slits of various sizes and orientations and circular holes were machined in the panels at the midsection and between the two buffer strips. Three types of loading situations were investigated during the program as shown in Table 1. The

TABLE 1—*Summary of the test program plan.*

| Loading History | Initial Flaw Description | | Panel Number |
	Type	Size, in.	
Static tension to crack initiation, arrest, and ultimate failure	none (control specimen)[a]	...	−1
	slit[b]	0.50	−3
	hole[c]	0.50	−5
	slit	0.75	−9
	hole	0.75	−6
	slit	1.00	−12
Static tension to crack initiation and arrest. Tensile fatigue in the arrested condition	slit	0.75	−10
	hole	0.75	−4
	slit	1.00	−11
Tensile fatigue, 10⁶ cycles, followed by static tension to crack initiation, arrest, and ultimate failure	slit	0.75	−8
	45° slit	0.75	−2
	hole	0.75	−7

[a]All panels were 8-ply $(0, +45,90)_s$ Thornel 300/SP286 graphite/epoxy with two ±45-deg buffer strips.
[b]All slits 1/16-in. wide with rounded ends.
[c]All holes circular and unloaded.

efficacy of the arrestment strips in these situations (two of which involve fatigue loading) is discussed in the next section.

Static Loading Test Results

As indicated in Table 1, six panels were tested under static load to failure. The test results are shown in Table 2. Note that all of the flawed panels tested failed at approximately 50 percent of the failure load for the unflawed panel. The results of Table 2 indicate that the crack initiation load decreases with damage size, a result consistent with fracture mechanics theory. Also, it appears that the geometric difference between a slit and a circular hole having a diameter equal to the slit length does not appreciably affect the crack initiation load. This has been observed previously for small to moderate slit and hole sizes [1, 3].

TABLE 2—Test results for panels subjected to static tensile loading only.

Panel Number	Initial Flaw	Load at Fast Crack Initiation, lb	Load at Panel Ultimate Failure, lb	Fast Crack Arrestment
−1	none	19 000	19 000	no
−3	0.50-in. slit	8 900	8 900	no
−5	0.50-in. hole	9 500	9 500	no
−9	0.75-in. slit	8 400	10 200	yes
−6	0.75-in. hole	7 500	9 500	yes
−12	1.00-in. slit	7 400	10 000	yes

For the present $\pi/4$ laminate panel design, the crack growth was arrested under static load when the initial flaw size was longer than 0.5 in. For panels with 0.75 and 1.00-in. size flaws, initial crack growth was arrested and the panels subsequently withstood approximately 20 percent more load. Upon fast crack initiation and arrest, the load being applied to the panel drops somewhat, because of the sudden change in the panel compliance and a resulting drop in the hydraulic pressure of the Baldwin test machine. The fast crack growth always occurred approximately normal to the applied tension, that is, directly toward the arrestment strips. Upon entering the buffer strips, the running crack typically turned 45-deg, aligning itself with one of the buffer strip principal material axes prior to arrestment. This can be seen in Figs. 2 and 3 which show Panel −9 in the arrested and failed conditions.

FIG. 2—*Test Panel −9 showing the arrested crack at 7000 lb load after reaching 8400 lb load.*

As shown in Fig. 2, the loads were introduced into the panels via bonded-on aluminum tabs which took the applied loads from the test machine in combined bearing and grip friction along two rows of six bolts each. The aluminum tab ends were feathered so as to minimize any stress build-up in the specimen near the tab ends. A nearly uniform strain state was achieved in the specimen away from the flaw as verified by extensive strain gage measurements.

The load-strain response of a typical crack arrestment panel is shown in Fig. 4. The load was applied until crack initiation and arrestment occurred. The panel was then unloaded, inspected, and reloaded to ultimate failure. For panel loads between 6000 and 8000 lb, loud cracking sounds were heard, but no visible cracks were observed. After crack initiation at 8400 lb, the load dropped to 7700 lb. Until this time, all gages showed approximately the same load-strain response. When the panel was unloaded and reloaded, Strain Gage 4 in the buffer strip zone showed almost twice the strain as Gages 1 and 3. This was the result of stress (and strain) concentration induced by the arrested crack in the buffer strip. When the load was increased beyond the crack initiation load of 8400 lb, loud cracking sounds were again heard and some crack growth was observed across the width of the buffer strips. This was confirmed by the increased strain measured by Gage 4 as shown in Fig. 4.

Post-Arrest Fatigue Test Results

The post-crack arrest performance of a structural item containing arrestment strips is of interest. If the structure is unable to endure service-related fatigue loads, the beneficial effects observed under static loading would be illusory. The capability to arrest cracks under fatigue loading was investigated for three of the panels and the test results are summarized in Table 3.

Each of the three panels listed in Table 3 was first loaded statically until a fast crack was initiated and arrested. Comparing Tables 2 and 3, it is seen that corresponding panels yielded similar results to within a 10 to 12 percent scatter band for fast crack initiation load. The panels of Table 3 were then fatigue cycled at $R = 0.1$ loading. Panels -10 and -4 were fatigued so that the maximum fatigue load was 80 and 81 percent, respectively, of the corresponding fast crack initiation load. Panel -11 was tested so that the maximum fatigue load was actually in excess of the fast crack initiation load. The results for the three panels of Table 3 indicate that the buffer strips can contain a crack for a sustained period of time. Panel -10 failed in fatigue after more than a million and a half cycles. The other two panels

FIG. 3—*Test Panel −9 after failure at 10 200 lb load.*

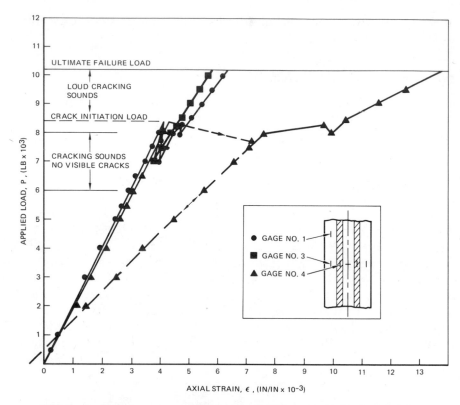

FIG. 4—*Load-strain response of test Panel −9 under static tension load to failure.*

sustained one million cycles and then exhibited residual strengths of approximately 90 percent of the corresponding nonfatigued but arrested panels of Table 2. As one would expect, the panels lose their pre-crack initiation identity upon arrestment. That is, Panels -9, -6, and -12 in Table 2 exhibit substantially the same ultimate failure loads. The same is true for Panels -4 and -11 of Table 3.

During the fatigue loading process, it was observed that the cracks tended to grow across the width of the buffer strips. In the case of Panel -10, the crack grew completely across the strip and fatigue failure resulted. The growth of the arrested crack was decidedly nonuniform; rather than a "crack growth rate," one would typically observe one or two jump increases in crack length prior to attaining a million cycles of loading.

Fatigue Loading and Subsequent Static Test Results

It has been observed [3–5] that a notched composite will apparently "heal" under tensile fatigue loading. That is, exposure to tensile fatigue

TABLE 3—*Test results for panels subjected to static tension until crack arrest occurred,
followed by tensile fatigue in the arrested condition.*

Panel Number	Initial Flaw	Load at Fast Crack Initiation, lb	Maximum Fatigue ($R = 0.1$) Load, lb	Fatigue Duration, cycles	Post-Fatigue Residual Strength, lb
−10	0.75-in. slit	7500	6000	1.534×10^6	specimen failed in fatigue
−4	0.75-in. hole	8300	6750	1.0×10^6	8600
−11	1.00-in. slit	6600	6750	1.0×10^6	8750

prior to static loading to failure appears to elevate the static failing stress.
During this portion of the test program, the "healing" phenomenon was
examined for the crack arrest configuration.

Testing was confined to the 0.75-in. notches shown in Table 4. As indicated, each specimen was initially subjected to tensile ($R = 0.1$) fatigue
for one million cycles. The maximum fatigue levels were set at high percentages (90 and 100 percent) of the fast crack initiation loads previously
established for panels which were tested statically. After the fatigue exposure,
the panels were subjected to static tension to failure. Significant "healing"
is in evidence when the fast crack initiation loads for Panels -9 and -8
(for slits) and Panels -6 and -7 (for holes) are compared.

As was the case for all panels for which an arrestment occurred, the
load dropped as the crack was initiated and arrested due to the panel compliance change and the characteristics of the loading machine. Each of the
panels in Table 4 experienced a load drop, and each also experienced a
crack arrestment. Upon increasing the load, ultimate panel failure occurred
at almost precisely the same load as did fast crack initiation. The fact that
the post-arrestment strength does not exceed the fast crack initiation load
suggests that in a load-controlled environment, an arrestment may not
have been achieved, particularly when the dynamic effect of a rapidly
running crack entering a buffer strip is considered. Note that the panel

TABLE 4—*Test results for panels subjected to tensile fatigue prior to applying
static tension to failure.*

Panel Number	Initial Flaw	Maximum Fatigue ($R = 0.1$) Load, lb	Fatigue Duration, cycles	Load at Fast Crack Initiation, lb	Load at Panel Ultimate Failure, lb
−8	0.75-in. slit	6750	10^6	9 600	9 500
−2	0.75-in. slit at 45°	6750	10^6	10 100	10 100
−7	0.75-in. hole	7500	10^6	9 300	9 300

failure loads with and without fatigue (that is, Panels -9, -6, and -12 in Table 2 and Panels -8, -2, and -7 in Table 4) exhibit comparable magnitudes. The 45-deg angle slit configuration tested exhibited approximately the same behavior as did the slit at right angles to the applied load. Examination of the arrested crack showed that the crack grew essentially normal to the applied load until it entered the buffer strip.

Two general observations were made during the test program. (1) All panels tended to buckle locally in areas above and below the cracks at high loads after crack arrestment. This was due to the transverse compression stress that developed around the crack region. (2) During fatigue cycling, surface temperature in the region around the crack increased. This was observed at the locations of large buckling amplitudes.

Fractographic Examination of the Failure Surface

The failure surfaces of Panels -8 and -9 were examined using the scanning electron microscope (SEM). The purpose of this examination was to investigate the failure modes of the fibers, the matrix and the fiber-matrix interface induced by static and fatigue load environments. This was done to determine if the "healing" associated with prefatiguing correlated with an altered fractographic appearance.

The load history of Panels -9 and -8 have been given in Tables 2 and 4, respectively. The failure surfaces are shown in the series of fractographs in Figs. 5 and 6 for Panels -9 and -8, respectively. For the two specimens, similar locations in the crack tip region are shown for comparison. Three types of failure modes were observed from the specimen fractographs:

1. The fatigue cycled Specimen -8 shows more fiber pullouts and fiber-matrix disbonds as compared to the static loaded Specimen -9. This type of failure has also been observed in boron/epoxy laminates [5].
2. The fatigue cycled specimen shows interlaminar shear failure near the crack tip region. This type of failure was not observed in the fractographs of the static loaded specimen.
3. The fatigue cycled specimen showed relatively more flat and sharp failure surfaces of the fiber ends as compared to the static loaded panel which showed rough failure surfaces of the fiber ends. This may be an indication of fatigue damage in the graphite fibers and requires further investigation.

These observed failure modes in the crack tip region have the combined effect of reducing the effective stress concentration and increasing the load at which failure initiation occurs for the fatigue cycled panels.

Analytical Predictions and Comparisons with Test Data

For a wide panel with multiple buffer strips, the panel load-stress rela-

FIG. 5—*Photomicrographs in the crack tip region of the failed Panel −9 (static tension loaded).*

tionships are readily obtained under the assumption of constant strain in the panel away from the crack. These are,

$$\sigma_1 = \frac{E_1}{(n+1)E_1 w_1 t_1 + nE_2 w_2 t_2} P \qquad (1)$$

and

$$\sigma_2 = \frac{E_2}{(n+1)E_1 w_1 t_1 + nE_2 w_2 t_2} P \qquad (2)$$

where Subscripts 1 and 2 identify the primary laminate and the buffer strip materials of the panel, respectively. Furthermore,

σ = laminate axial stress,
P = panel applied load,

FIG. 6—*Photomicrographs in the crack tip region of the failed Panel −8 (prefatigued).*

E = elastic modulus,
w = width of individual laminate sections,
t = laminate thickness, and
$n\,(\geqslant 2)$ = number of buffer strips in the panel.

The load-stress relations for the particular panel geometry and laminate properties used in the present test program are calculated from Eqs 1 and 2. The elastic properties and geometry for the 8-ply (0, ±45, 90)$_s$ Thornel 300/SP286 laminated panel are

$$E_1 = 7.3 \times 10^6 \text{ psi} \qquad E_2 = 2.5 \times 10^6 \text{ psi}$$

$$w_1 = 2.0 \text{ in.} \qquad w_2 = 1.0 \text{ in.}$$

$$t_1 = t_2 = 0.044 \text{ in.} \qquad n = 2$$

Substituting these values into Eqs 1 and 2, the load-stress relations are

$$\sigma_1 = 3.40 \times P \text{ psi} \qquad (3)$$

$$\sigma_2 = 1.16 \times P \text{ psi} \qquad (4)$$

The panel stresses calculated with the use of Eqs 3 and 4 are summarized in Table 5.

TABLE 5—*Stresses in the buffer strip panels at fast crack initiation and ultimate fracture.*

Panel Number	Static Stresses at Initial Fracture		Ultimate Strength after Crack Arrestment	
	σ_1, ksi [a]	σ_2, ksi [b]	σ_1, ksi	σ_2, ksi
−1	64.5	22.0	...	...
−3	30.2	10.3	...	...
−5	32.3	11.0	...	...
−9	28.6	9.7	34.7	11.8
−6	25.5	8.7	32.3	11.0
−12	25.2	8.5	34.0	11.6
−10	25.5	8.7	...	...
−4	28.2	9.6	29.2	10.0
−11	22.4	7.6	29.8	10.1
−8	32.6	11.1	32.3	11.0
−2	34.3	11.7	34.3	11.7
−7	31.6	10.8	31.6	10.8

[a] σ_1 = stress in primary laminate.
[b] σ_2 = stress in buffer strips.

For prediction of the composite panel fracture strength under applied static loading, the linear elastic fracture mechanics (LEFM) approach presented in Ref *4* is used. The justifications for the use of the LEFM approach for advanced composite materials have been discussed in the recent literature [3,6] and are not repeated here. Accordingly, the critical applied stress at which a fast crack propagates from an initial slit of length 2*l* in an infinite width panel, not considering the geometric effect of the buffer strips, is given by

$$\sigma_c = \frac{K_Q}{\sqrt{\pi(l + a)}} \qquad (5)$$

where K_Q is the candidate fracture toughness of the material and a is the characteristic dimension of the intense energy region that is assumed to exist at the ends of the slit. These two parameters are determined from the test data for failure strength of a control specimen and a specimen with central slit by using the equations

$$a = \frac{l}{\left(\dfrac{\sigma_\infty}{\sigma_c}\right)^2 - 1} \tag{6}$$

$$K_Q = \sigma_\infty \sqrt{\pi a} \tag{7}$$

where σ_∞ is the failure stress in the primary laminate of the unflawed specimen.

The fracture parameters for the primary laminate are calculated, using Eqs 6 and 7, and the test data given in Table 5 for the control Panel -1 and the average of Panels -9 and -10 with 0.75-in. slits.

$$a_1 = \frac{0.375}{(64\,500/27\,050)^2 - 1} = 0.08 \text{ in.} \tag{8}$$

$$K_{Q1} = 64\,500 \times \sqrt{\pi \times 0.08} = 32\,300 \text{ psi}\sqrt{\text{in.}} \tag{9}$$

The critical crack initiation stress in the primary laminate for identical specimens with any slit of length $2l$ can then be predicted by substituting the values of a_1 and K_{Q1} into Eq 5

$$\sigma_{1c} = \frac{32\,300}{\sqrt{\pi(l + 0.08)}} \text{ psi} \tag{10}$$

The expression for critical running load as a function of the critical crack propagation stress is obtained by modifying Eq 3

$$N_c = 0.0367 \times \sigma_{1c} \text{ lb/in.} \tag{11}$$

Note that for wider panels of identical geometry but with proportionately more buffer strips, the running load-stress relation is not significantly different from Eq 11. For example, for a panel with $n = 4$, $N_c = 0.0357 \times \sigma_{1c}$ lb/in. and for a panel with $n = 6$, $N_c = 0.0353 \times \sigma_{1c}$ lb/in. Note further that if the number of buffer strips is increased for a fixed panel width, the load distribution between the primary and the buffer strip materials would change. Hence, the multiplier term in the load-stress Eq 11 would also change and the crack initiation loads would be different.

An upper bound for ultimate strength of the panel with an arrested crack is readily calculated if it is assumed that the stress concentration effect is confined to the buffer strips. Then the upper bound for ultimate strength N_{ub} is simply the strength of the remaining uncracked panel and is given by

$$N_{ub} = \sigma_\infty \left[nw_1 t_1 + (n - 2) \left(\frac{E_2}{E_1} \right) w_2 t_2 \right] \quad [(n + 1)w_1 + nw_2] \quad (12)$$

For the present panel design with $n = 2$, $N_{ub} = 1420$ lb/in. For wider panels with proportionately more buffer strips, higher values of N_{ub} are obtained. For example, for a panel with $n = 4$, $N_{ub} = 1756$ lb/in., and for a panel with $n = 6$, $N_{ub} = 1900$ lb/in.

The predicted and test loads for initial fracture and ultimate strength of the test panels are plotted as functions of the slit length in Fig. 7. The predicted initial fracture load curves for values of $n = 2$, 4, and 6 are approximately coincident. For wider panels the higher upper bound values of ultimate strength are shown. Good agreement is found between predicted values and test data for initial fracture strength. Test data for fatigue cycled panels are also plotted for comparison.

Conclusions

The results of the present test program have shown that the buffer strip concept is capable of providing fracture control in graphite/epoxy laminates

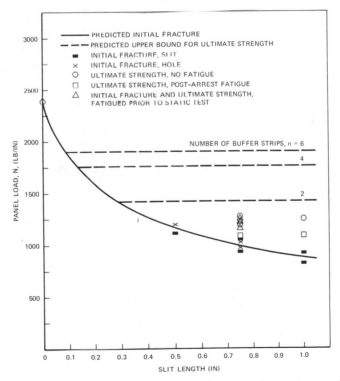

FIG. 7—*Initial fracture and ultimate strength of buffer strip panels as a function of initial flaw size.*

under both static and fatigue load environments. The crack arrestment capability, however, depends on the initial flaw size. After crack arrestment, any additional load carrying capability depends on the width of the panel and the number of buffer strips. For wider panels with a proportionately larger number of buffer strips, higher ultimate strength is indicated. However, this needs to be verified by further tests. The LEFM theory provides a reliable tool for predicting the initial fracture strength. The fatigue tests have shown that after crack arrestment, the buffer strips can contain a crack for a sustained period of fatigue loading and still have significant residual strength.

Fatigue loading of initially flawed panels increases the subsequent static load crack initiation strength. This is attributed to the "healing" effect in the crack tip region. Fractographic comparison of the crack tip regions for static loaded and fatigued panels has shown that for fatigued panels more fiber pullouts, fiber-matrix disbonds, interlaminar shear failures, and distinctly sharp failure surfaces of the fiber ends occur.

References

[1] Eisenmann, J. R. and Kaminski, B. E., *Engineering Fracture Mechanics,* Vol. 4, 1972, pp. 907–913.
[2] Erdogan, F. and Gupta, G. D., "On the Bounds for the Stress Intensity Factors in Laminated Composites," NASA Report TR-72-14, Lehigh University, Bethlehem, Pa., July 1973.
[3] Halpin, J. C., Jerina, K. L., and Johnson, T. A. in *Analysis of the Test Methods for High Modulus Fibers and Composites, ASTM STP 521,* American Society of Testing and Materials, 1973, pp. 5–64.
[4] Waddoups, M. E., Eisenmann, J. R., and Kaminski, B. E., *Journal of Composite Materials,* Vol. 5, 1971, p. 446.
[5] Durchlaub, E. C. and Freeman, R. B., "Design Data for Composite Structure Safelife Prediction," Technical Report AFML-TR-73-225, Air Force Materials Laboratory, Dayton, Ohio, March 1974.
[6] Konish, H. J., Swedlow, J. L., and Cruse, T. A., *AIAA Journal,* Vol. 11, No. 1, 1973, pp. 40–43.

G. P. Sendeckyj[1]

Concepts for Crack Arrestment in Composites

REFERENCE: Sendeckyj, G. P., "Concepts for Crack Arrestment in Composites," *Fracture Mechanics of Composites, ASTM STP 593,* American Society for Testing and Materials, 1975, pp. 215–226.

ABSTRACT: Crack arrestment criteria for composite panels containing buffer (or crack-arrestment) strips are derived for the cases of cracks within the primary and buffer-strip material. The criteria, which can be used to size the buffer strips to arrest cracks of given length, are in good agreement with the available experimental data on crack arrest in composite panels.

KEY WORDS: fracture properties, composite materials, stresses, laminates, crack propagation, crack arrest, damage control

Advanced high-performance fiber-reinforced composite materials are normally thought of as being brittle solids, with the brittleness being reflected in low fracture toughness and impact energy absorption capability. Due to their brittle nature, composites are susceptible to foreign object damage. Hence, material design concepts for improving the damage tolerance of composites are of considerable interest.

One such concept, proposed in the literature [1–4],[2] is the use of crack-arrestment strips. Basically, this concept consists of replacing strips of selected laminas in a multi-directional laminate by strips of different fiber orientations of the same material [1–3] or another material system [4]. In both cases, the crack-arrestment strips introduce macroscopic variations of stiffness and fracture toughness into the multi-directional laminate. This affects the crack-tip stress-intensity factors and strain-energy release rates of propagating cracks. If the crack-arrestment strips introduce sufficiently large local variations in crack-tip stress-intensity factors, a

[1]Aerospace engineer, Fatigue, Fracture, and Reliability Group, Structural Integrity Branch, Structures Division, Air Force Flight Dynamics Laboratory, Wright-Patterson AFB, Ohio 45433.
[2]The italic numbers in brackets refer to the list of references appended to this paper.

running crack will be arrested. Upon subsequent loading, reinitiation of crack propagation will take place at higher loads or will be delayed for some time under cyclic loading. If the time required to reinitiate crack propagation is sufficiently long, the use of crack-arrestment strips will provide a degree of fail safety capability.

The optimum design of multi-directional laminates containing crack-arrestment strips is complicated by the large number of possible variables, among which we have:

1. laminate loading conditions and type of damage initiating crack propagation,
2. laminate stacking sequence and ply orientations,
3. width of the crack-arrestment strips,
4. location of the crack-arrestment strips relative to the damage, and
5. crack-arrestment strip material.

Moreover, because of the crack size effects observed in composite materials, the critical stress-intensity factors depend on crack length [5] and, hence, laminates containing small-scale damage are expected to behave differently from those containing large-scale damage. Thus, different crack-arrestment strip configurations may have to be used for different expected damage zone sizes.

The choice of material used in the crack-arrestment strips affects the macroscopic stiffness and fracture toughness variations within the laminate. Since (1) cracks tend to run into softer regions and to be arrested upon approaching stiffer ones and (2) the softer regions carry a lower share of the panel load, the crack-arrestment strip material should be chosen to accentuate the stiffness variation. This can be done by using as low a modulus material as possible for the crack-arrestment strips. In this case, the crack would run into the low-modulus region and be arrested as it approaches the high-modulus region. In addition to buffer strips (lower modulus strips), crack arrestment can be achieved by local stiffening or by local thickness build-up [6], which has the same effect as selectively increasing the laminate stiffness. This is normally done in metallic structures, such as, stringer reinforced panels [7–10].

The fracture toughness variation in the crack-arrestment panel also plays a role in crack arrestment. A crack running into a tougher region will be arrested. Hence, the crack-arrestment strips should be as tough as possible.

In the present work, various crack-arrestment concepts are first reviewed. Then, a crack-arrestment criterion is derived for the longitudinal buffer-strip configuration. Two cases are considered, namely, a crack in the primary laminate and a crack within the buffer strip. Based on the arrestment criterion, a method for designing crack-arrestment panels for various expected damage sizes is outlined.

Crack-Arrestment Strip Concepts

Three crack-arrestment concepts have been investigated in the literature. These are:

1. replace selected strips of 0° plies of the primary laminate with ±45° plies of the same material [1, 3];
2. replace selected strips of 0° plies of primary laminate with 0° plies of a lower modulus material [4]; and
3. adhesively bond additional material at selected locations of the primary laminate [6].

The first concept was used to demonstrate crack arrestment in boron-epoxy [1] and graphite-epoxy [3] laminates. In both cases, 1-in.-wide strips of the (0°/±45°/90°) primary laminate were replaced with (±45°) crack-arrestment (buffer) strips. The unsoftened strips of the primary laminate were 2-in. wide. In both cases, long cracks in the primary laminate were arrested while short ones were not. Moreover, the crack-arrestment capability was achieved at a stiffness and strength penalty.

The second concept also successfully arrested cracks [4]. In this case, the stiffness and strength penalty is not as great as in the first concept. Finally, the third concept shows a crack-arrestment capability, but at a weight penalty.

Even though these concepts provide crack-arrestment capability, they do so at the expense of stiffness and weight penalties. One concept that has not been attempted heretofore is to replace selected strips of the plies at angular orientations. (for example, ±45° plies) to the load direction with another material. This should provide a crack-arrestment capability without an appreciable weight and stiffness penalty.

Consider, for example, a (0°/±45°) laminate loaded in the 0° direction. According to nonlinear laminated plate analysis, the ±45° plies contribute little to the axial stiffness and strength. Hence, replacing selected strips of the ±45° plies with a lower modulus, high fracture toughness material will not decrease appreciably the axial stiffness and strength of the laminate. Thus, the proposed hybrid laminate configuration is expected to have essentially the same properties as the primary laminate.

In this concept, crack arrestment is expected to occur by a crack path deflection mechanism as opposed to the mechanism operating in the other crack-arrestment concepts. The propagating crack is expected to be deflected by the buffer strips into a path parallel to the load direction and stopped by the other arrestment strips. Moreover, crack propagation should not be reinitiated under post-arrest fatigue loading. Whether this concept will actually work has to be determined experimentally. A test program to verify this concept is being planned and experimental results should be available in the near future.

Analysis of Longitudinal Crack-Arrestment Strip Concept

Consider the crack-arrestment panel, consisting of $(2n + 1)$ strips of primary laminate interspersed with $2n$ crack-arrestment strips, as shown in Fig. 1. Let quantities referring to the crack-arrestment strips be distinguished by an asterisk from those referring to the primary laminate. Let K_{Ic}, a, E, w, and t denote the critical stress intensity factor, size of the high energy zone at the crack tip, longitudinal Young's modulus, width, and thickness of the strips of the laminate, respectively. K_{Ic} and a are the parameters proposed by Waddoups et al [11] to take into account the crack size effect. Subscripts i will be used to distinguish the individual strips of the panel whenever necessary.

Assume that a crack of initial length, 2ℓ, is present in the center strip, as shown in Fig. 1. This crack will propagate at a critical load level, P_I. Assume that this crack grows to a total length, $2L$, at which it is arrested. The residual strength, P_R, of the panel is defined as the load at which the arrested crack would start to propagate again. Hence, for successful crack arrest to occur, we must have

$$P_R > P_I \tag{1}$$

This condition, in conjunction with engineering estimates of the critical stress levels at which the original crack of length 2ℓ and the arrested crack of length $2L$ would propagate, is used in this section to derive an inequality in terms of material variables that governs crack arrestment.

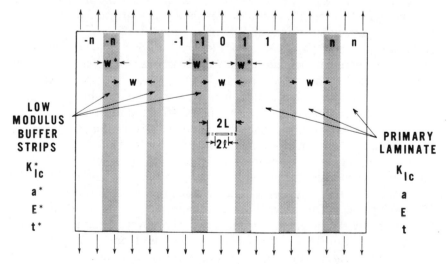

FIG. 1—*Crack-arrestment panel with a crack of length 2ℓ in parent material. After arrestment occurs, the crack has length $2L$.*

Assuming that the panel is gripped with rigid grips, we have that the far-field longitudinal strains are identical in all the strips, that is

$$e_0 = e_i = e^*_i = e, \qquad (i = \pm 1, \pm 2, \ldots \pm n) \tag{2}$$

Upon further assuming that the panel is sufficiently long so that a compliance correction does not have to be made for the cracked strip of primary material, the far-field longitudinal stresses are related to the longitudinal strains by

$$e_0 = e_i = \sigma_i/E, \qquad e^*_i = \sigma^*_i/E^* \tag{3}$$

from which follows that

$$\sigma_i{}^* = \gamma\sigma_i = \gamma\sigma_0 \tag{4}$$

where $\gamma = E^*/E$ is the ratio of Young's moduli. If the panel is short, a correction has to be made to take into account the increased compliance of the cracked strip due to the presence of the crack. Neglecting the compliance correction has the effect of making the crack-arrestment criterion slightly unconservative for short panels and has no effect on the criterion for long ones.

Now the initial crack (length 2ℓ) will propagate when

$$\sigma_0[\pi(\ell + a)]^{1/2}f(\ell/w) = K_{1c} \tag{5}$$

Herein, $f(\ell/w)$ is the correction for finite width of the cracked strip. Even though the effect of the buffer strips on either side of the cracked strip should be taken into account, no method is known for doing this without performing a finite-element analysis of the complete panel. Hence, the correction factor for a crack in a finite width strip will be used, that is

$$f(\ell/w) = [1 - (2\ell/w)^2]^{-1/2} \tag{6}$$

This correction factor is readily derived by a method attributed to Filon for approximating the stress concentration factors for cutouts in finite width plates [12]. In view of all the other assumptions being made, this is sufficiently accurate for our purpose.

Upon substituting Eq 6 into Eq 5 and solving for σ_0, we have

$$\sigma_0 = K_{1c}[1 - (2\ell/w)^2]^{1/2}[\pi(\ell + a)]^{-1/2} \tag{7}$$

at incipient crack extension. Hence, the load at incipient crack extension is given by

$$\begin{aligned}
P_1 &= (2n + 1)tw\sigma_0 + 2nt^*w^*\sigma^* \\
&= [(2n + 1)tw + 2nt^*w^*\gamma]K_{1c}[1 - (2\ell/w)^2]^{1/2} \times [\pi(\ell + a)]^{-1/2} \tag{8}
\end{aligned}$$

To estimate the residual load carrying capacity of the panel, assume that the crack has length $2L$ ($\geqslant w$) after being arrested. Moreover, assume that the failed primary strip (Strip 0 in Fig. 1) remains bonded to the two buffer strips on either side and behaves like the buffer material. Thus, the arrested crack can be modeled as a crack of length $2L$ in a strip of buffer material ($w + 2w^*$) in width. The fracture criterion applied to this strip gives

$$\sigma^* = K_{Ic}^*\{1 - [2L/(w + 2w^*)]^2\}^{1/2}[\pi(L + a^*)]^{-1/2} \qquad (9)$$

at incipient extension of the arrested crack. Hence, the residual load is given by

$$P_R = 2ntw\sigma_0 + 2nt^*w^*\sigma^* + tw\sigma^*$$

$$= K_{Ic}^*[2ntw/\gamma + 2nt^*w^* + tw]$$

$$\times \{1 - [2L/(w + 2w^*)]^2\}^{1/2}[\pi(L + a^*)]^{-1/2} \qquad (10)$$

Upon substituting Eqs 8 and 10 into Eq 1, the condition for successful crack arrest becomes

$$[2n(tw + t^*w^*\gamma) + tw\gamma]\{1 - [2L/(w + 2w^*)]^2\}^{1/2}[1 + a]^{1/2}K_{Ic}^*$$

$$> [(2n + 1)tw + 2nt^*w^*\gamma][1 - (2\ell/w)^2][L + a^*]^{1/2}\gamma K_{Ic} \qquad (11)$$

Let us now assume that the running crack is arrested as it enters the buffer strip (that is, when $L = w/2$), as was done in Ref 1. Upon setting $L = w/2$ in Eq 11, the crack-arrestment criterion simplifies to

$$[2n(tw + t^*w^*\gamma) + tw\gamma]\{1 - [w/(w + 2w^*)]^2\}^{1/2}[\ell + a]^{1/2}K_{Ic}^*$$

$$> [(2n + 1)tw + 2nt^*w^*\gamma][1 - (2\ell/w)^2]^{1/2}[w/2 + a^*]^{1/2}\gamma K_{Ic} \qquad (12)$$

It should be noted that assuming $L = w/2$ tends to be unconservative. This follows from the observation that as L increases, the left-hand side of the inequality decreases, while the right-hand side increases in magnitude. The experimental observations made in Ref 3 suggest that it is more realistic to assume that $2L \cong w + w^*/2$. Since the distance the arrested crack extends into the buffer strip depends on panel configuration, the assumption that $L = w/2$ will be retained in the present work.

The crack-arrestment criterion, Eq 12, is valid for panels containing an arbitrary number of buffer strips. In actual applications, the panels are expected to have a large number of buffer strips. Hence, Eq 12 can be simplified by taking the limit as $n \to \infty$. In this limit, the crack-arrestment criterion becomes

$$\{1 - [w/(w + 2w^*)]^2\}^{1/2}[l + a]^{1/2}K_{Ic}^* > [1 - (2l/w)^2]^{1/2} \tag{13}$$
$$\times [w/2 + a^*]^{1/2}\gamma K_{Ic}$$

In contrast to the criterion given in Ref *1*, the present crack-arrestment criterion can be used to size the buffer strip for a given damage zone size as measured by the initial crack length $2l$. Alternately, it can be used to determine the minimum initial length of a crack that can be arrested successfully in a given panel configuration.

The previous derived crack-arrestment criterion is applicable to the case of an initial crack for (or any other through-the-thickness damage) confined to a strip of the primary material. Even though this criterion can be used for design purposes, it is not valid for panels in which the buffer strip is cracked initially. Since the derivation of the crack arrestment criterion for this case follows, with minor modifications, the procedure just used, only the final results will be given here. If the initial crack lies completely within the buffer strip $(2l < w^*)$ and is arrested on entering the next set of buffer strips after failing the two adjacent primary strips, the crack-arrestment criterion is

$$\{1 - [(2w + w^*)/(2w + 3w^*)]^2\}^{1/2}[l + a^*]^{1/2} \tag{14}$$
$$> [1 - (2l/w^*)^2]^{1/2}[w + w^*/2 + a^*]^{1/2}$$

If the initial crack cutting the buffer strip terminates within the strips of primary material $(w^* < 2l < 2w + w^*)$ and is arrested on entering the next set of buffer strips, the criterion for crack arrestment becomes

$$\{1 - [(2w + w^*)/(2w + 3w^*)]^2\}^{1/2}[l + a]^{1/2}K_{Ic}^*$$
$$> \{1 - [2l/(2w + w^*)]^2\}^{1/2}[w + w^*/2 + a^*]^{1/2}\gamma K_{Ic} \tag{15}$$

Upon examining the three crack-arrestment criteria, we see that Criterion 14 is most severe. It indicates that only cracks almost completely severing the buffer strip can be arrested, but even then on physical grounds crack arrest is highly unlikely. Criterion 15 is more severe than Criterion 13 and, hence, it should be used in designing the crack-arrestment panels.

Upon examining the crack-arrestment criteria, it is seen that for the greatest degree of damage tolerance the buffer strips should have the lowest possible stiffness and highest possible fracture toughness. This information can be used to screen candidate buffer-strip materials. Moreover, on physical grounds the buffer-strip material should be selected in such a way as to avoid cut fibers in the laminate.

Theory-Experiment Comparison

The experimental data, necessary for a complete verification of the present crack-arrestment criteria, must consist of (1) initial fracture and residual strengths for a crack-arrestment panel with cracks of various lengths and (2) independently determined fracture toughness (K_{Ic} and $K*_{Ic}$) and high energy zone sizes (a and $a*$) for the primary and buffer-strip materials. Even though the initial fracture and residual strengths for crack-arrestment panels are avaliable in the literature [1, 3], valid fracture toughness characteristics of the primary and buffer-strip materials have not been reported. This makes any theory-experiment comparison tenuous at best. Keeping these comments in mind, let us compare the predictions of the crack-arrestment criteria with the available experimental data.

All the available experimental data are for 8-in. (20.32-cm) wide, (($P.I._{\pm 45°/90°}$) panels with two 1-in. (2.54-cm) wide buffer strips of ± 45 material spaced 2 in. (5.08 cm) apart. In these panels, the ± 45 plies within the primary material are continuous throughout the complete panel, while the 0° and 90° plies which would normally occupy the area reserved for the buffer strips are omitted and replaced by either a $\pm 45°$ or a $-45°$ ply maintaining symmetry about the laminate mid-plane.

The boron-epoxy panels [1] were 0.085 in. (2.16 mm) thick, 16 in. (4.06 cm) long, and had a modulus ratio $\gamma = 2.42/11.39$. Slits of three different lengths were machined perpendicular to the loading direction in the center strip of the primary material. The panels were loaded at constant strain rate until fast crack propagation from the initial slit occurred to determine the panel fracture initiation load, P_I. If crack arrest occurred, the panels were inspected and retested to failure to determine the residual strength, P_R.

The experimental results, taken from Ref 1, are compared with the theoretical predictions in Table 1. Since valid fracture data for the primary and buffer-strip materials are not available, K_{Ic} and a values were estimated, using Eq 8, from the experimental values of fracture initiation loads (P_I) for the panels with 0.00 and 0.65 in. (1.65 cm) slit. The estimated values

$$K_{Ic} = 34\ 214 \text{ psi } \sqrt{\text{in.}}\ (37.6\ \text{MNm}^{-2}\sqrt{\text{m}})$$
$$a = 0.0907 \text{ in. } (2.3 \text{ mm})$$

were then used to predict P_I for the other slit lengths. The residual strength was predicted, using Eq 10, by assuming that $a* = a$, and $K_{Ic}* = 22\ 000 \text{ psi}\sqrt{\text{in.}}$ (24.2 MNm$^{-2}\sqrt{\text{m}}$). The value of $K_{Ic}*$ was taken from Ref 2.

As can be seen from Table 1, the theoretical predictions are in good agreement with the experimental data. With respect to P_I, this is not surprising because any fracture type criterion would fit the fracture initiation data. The excellent agreement between the predicted and experimental values of P_R tends to support the validity of the present crack-arrestment criterion because:

1. $K_{Ic}*$ and $a*$ were estimated independently and, hence, satisfy the requirement for verification of the theoretical predictions.
2. $a*$ is consistent in magnitude with a. This indicates that the two-parameter description of fracture initiation used in the derivations is probably a valid description of the fracture characteristics of composite materials.
3. The predicted value of P_R is higher than the experimental values. This is consistent with the expected unconservatism of the criterion due to the assumption on the length of the arrested crack. In fact, it was observed [1] that the crack extended somewhat into the buffer strips. Taking this observation into account would lower the predicted value of P_R and, hence, make the agreement even better.

The graphite-epoxy panels [3] were 0.044 in. (1.12 mm) thick, 20 in. (50.8 cm) long, and had a modulus ratio $\gamma = 2.5/7.3$. Panels with three different slit lengths were tested at constant strain rate. The experimental results are compared with theoretical predictions in Table 2. As was done for the boron-epoxy data, K_{Ic} and a were estimated from the fracture initiation load data and the estimated values

$$K_{Ic} = 38\ 040\ \mathrm{psi}\sqrt{\mathrm{in.}}\ (41.8\ \mathrm{MNm}^{-\frac{3}{2}}\sqrt{\mathrm{m}})$$
$$a = 0.11\ \mathrm{in.}\ (2.79\ \mathrm{mm})$$

were used to predict P_I. As can be seen from Table 2, the agreement between theory and experiment is good. Moreover, the value of K_{Ic} is approximately one-half the longitudinal strength. This is consistent with Nuismer's conjecture [13] that the fracture toughness is one-half the tensile strength of the laminate. The predicted value of P_R is based on assuming $a* = a$ and $K_{Ic}* = 28\ 000\ \mathrm{psi}\ \sqrt{\mathrm{in.}}\ (30.8\ \mathrm{MNm}^{-2}\sqrt{\mathrm{m}})$.

As can be seen from Table 2, the agreement between the predicted and experimentally measured values of P_R is not as good for the graphite-epoxy panels as for the boron-epoxy ones. This lack of agreement is a direct consequence of the delamination and crack branching that occurred in the $\pm 45°$ graphite-epoxy buffer strips [3]. Hence, the residual strength cannot be predicted by Eq 10. It must be predicted by assuming that the primary material in the undamaged strips of the panel carry all the load, that is

$$P_R = 2wt\sigma_{ult} \tag{16}$$

where σ_{ult} is the tensile strength of the primary material. Using the data in Table 2 and solving for σ_{ult}, we get $\sigma_{ult}, = 64\ 100\ \mathrm{psi}$ which is close to the expected value of the ultimate strength of the primary material. This shows that crack arrestment can be achieved by the natural crack blunting associated with extensive delamination.

TABLE 1—*Theory-experiment comparison for boron-epoxy crack-arrestment panels.*

Slit Length, $2l$	Fracture Initiation Load, P_I		Residual Strength, P_R	
	Experiment	Theory	Experiment	Theory
0.00 in (0.00 cm)	35 000 lb (155.75 KN)	35 000 lb (155.75 KN)	...	...
0.14 in (0.36 cm)	26 600 lb (118.37 KN)	26 470 lb (117.79 KN)	...	...
0.45 in (1.14 cm)	16 750 lb (74.54 KN)	18 450 lb (82.10 KN)	19 350 lb (86.11 KN)	19 970 lb (88.87 KN)
0.65 in (1.65 cm)	15 900 lb (70.76 KN)	15 600 lb (69.42 KN)	19 000 lb (84.55 KN)	19 970 lb (88.87 KN)

TABLE 2—*Theory-experiment comparison for graphite-epoxy crack-arrestment panels.*

Slit Length, $2l$	Fracture Initiation Load, P_I		Residual Strength, P_R	
	Experiment	Theory	Experiment	Theory
0.00 in (0.00 cm)	19 000 lb (84.55 KN)	19 000 lb (84.55 KN)	...	...
0.50 in (1.27 cm)	8 900 lb (39.61 KN)	10 182 lb (45.31 KN)	10 200 lb (45.39 KN)	8 960 lb (39.87 KN)
0.75 in (1.91 cm)	8 400 lb (37.38 KN)	8 400 lb (37.38 KN)	10 000 lb (44.50 KN)	8 900 lb (39.87 KN)
1.00 in (2.54 cm)	7 400 lb (32.93 KN)	6 998 lb (31.14 KN)		

Discussion and Conclusion

Crack-arrestment criteria, based on the two-parameter description of fracture in composites proposed by Waddoups et al [11], have been derived for various cases of initial damage in panels containing buffer strips. The criteria require a priori knowledge of the fracture parameters for the primary and buffer-strip materials. With these parameters known, the criteria can be used to size the buffer strips to arrest any size initial crack. Alternately, for a given panel configuration, the criteria can be used to establish the minimum length of a crack that can be arrested successfully by the buffer strip.

A number of assumptions were made in deriving the crack-arrestment criteria. While most of these were made to simplify the derivations, the assumption about the length of the arrested crack was made on the basis of the derivations presented in Ref 1. As pointed out during the derivations, this assumption tends to make the crack-arrestment criteria unconservative. Hence, in practice the minimum width of the buffer strip must be taken greater than that specified by the criteria. As an alternative to making allowances for this unconservatism of the criteria, the length $2L$ of the arrested crack can be taken to be greater than $2w^* + w$. Since there is a lack of experimental data on the actual length of the arrested crack, it is best to use the criteria in their present form, keeping in mind that they are slightly unconservative.

The procedure for designing damage-tolerant panels is straightforward once the fracture characteristics of the primary and buffer-strip materials are known. Assuming the width of the primary strips and size of damage (as measured by the equivalent crack), Eqs 13 thru 15 can be used to size the buffer strips. In practice, the buffer strips should be sized such that damage confined strictly to the buffer strip cannot occur since this would place an overly stringent restriction on strip dimensions and material variables. For typical ballistic damage, the damage zone size will normally be greater than the buffer-strip width and, hence, the constraints of inequality 14 would not have to be imposed. Thus, Eq 15 which is more stringent than Eq 13 should be used to size the buffer strips.

Finally, the available experimental data for the boron-epoxy crack-arrestment panels compares well with the theoretical predictions. While the predictions based on Eq 10 are in poor agreement with the experimental data for the graphite-epoxy panels, Eq 16 predicts results that are in excellent agreement with the data. This implies that when extensive delamination occurs during crack arrest, the assumption that the crack retains its identity as a crack is erroneous. In that case, a simple mechanics of materials prediction is indicated.

The incompleteness of the data prevents us from making a proper theory-experiment comparison. For such a comparison, carefully-designed experiments with independently determined fracture characteristics of the primary laminate and buffer-strip materials must be performed. Such an experimental program is being planned and results should be available in the near future.

References

[1] Eisenmann, J. R. and Kaminski, B. E., *Engineering Fracture Mechanics,* Vol. 4, 1972, pp. 907–913.
[2] Eisenmann, J. R., "1972 Composite Wing Fracture Control," Report No. ERR-FW-1376, General Dynamics/Convair Aerospace Division, Jan. 1973.
[3] Bhatia, N. M. and Verette, R. M. in this symposium.
[4] McQuillan, E. and Huang, J., private communication.
[5] Konish, H. J., Jr. and Cruse, T. A. in *Composite Reliability, ASTM STP 580,* American Society for Testing and Materials, 1975.
[6] Slepetz, J., private communication.
[7] Romualdi, J. P. and Sanders, P. H., "Fracture Arrest by Riveted Stiffeners," AFOSR TR 60-174, Carnegie Institute of Technology, Oct. 1960.
[8] Isida, M. and Itagaki, Y., "Stress Concentration of the Tip of the Central Transverse Crack in a Stiffened Plate Subjected to Tension," *Proceedings,* Fourth U.S. National Congress of Applied Mechanics, Vol. 2, 1962.
[9] Poe, C. C., Jr. in *Proceedings,* Air Force Conference on Fatigue and Fracture of Aircraft Structures and Materials, AFFDL-TR-70-144, Dec. 1969, pp. 207–215.
[10] Vlieger, H., "Residual Strength of Cracked Stiffened Panels," NLR-TR-71004U, National Aerospace Laboratory, Netherlands, Jan. 1971.
[11] Waddoups, M. E., Eisenmann, J. R., and Kaminski, B. E., *Journal of Composite Materials,* Vol. 5, 1971, pp. 446–454.
[12] Hoskin, B. C., "Applications of Elasticity Theory in Fracture Studies of Cracked Sheet," Structures and Materials Report 294, Aeronautical Research Laboratories, Australia, Sept. 1963.
[13] Nuismer, R., private communication.